Mary
of
Nazareth

Mary
of
Nazareth

by
Esther Kellner

Appleton-Century-Crofts, Inc.
New York

for my teacher
MISS ANNA FINFROCK

Psalms 119:105

Mary
of
Nazareth

I.

WITH THE RISING OF THE SUN, THE NARROW STREETS OF THE village would be restored to life. Smoke from the early fires would drift from open doorways, blue and thin and fragrant on the cool morning air. Sheep and goats, hurried and clamorous, would be driven past the houses to the pasture beyond. Children would run to their play, women would trudge to the well, their water jars upon their shoulders, old men would sit upon the doorsills, dreaming in the sun, lads would go forth, with slow and reluctant steps, to the lessons of the law. Yet, in this moment, Nazareth slumbered, gleaming with dew, veiled in drifting mist, while the first radiance of dawn came to the unclouded sky.

A light wind had risen, bearing the damp sweetness of wild flowers, of olive groves and vineyards, of pale and blossoming shrubs. A single cock crew, and then another. Birds stirred within their nests and one poured forth sudden flowing notes of song. From the rooftops came the plaintive and familiar voices of the doves.

At the edge of the quiet village, sheltered by the silvery boughs of an olive grove, was the small house wherein dwelt the girl, Mary of Nazareth, and her widowed mother, Anne. Greatly wearied, Anne was yet deep in slumber, but Mary had been awake for some time, lying quietly upon her bed mat beneath the open window, her lips moving gently as she ut-

1

tered the familiar words of morning prayer. In this manner was begun the day of every person in the village, even in the province itself. Indeed, there was a saying concerning those of the province: *In Galilee, wealth means less than honor and goodness.*

The girl was very young, being less than fourteen years of age, small and slight, having an olive skin warmly tinted by the sun, wide clear eyes and dark hair which fell, gleaming, upon her shoulders and below. She was a girl of more than ordinary grace and beauty, of more than ordinary gentleness and humility. And though there was a look of fragility about her, she was not unaccustomed to burdensome toil for, seeing that her father had died, and her mother was both aged and ailing, the duties of the household lay heavy upon her small shoulders.

Her prayers being ended, she lay for a little time looking up at the window. The sill was deep, inasmuch as the walls of the house were of greater thickness than the length of a man's arm. Beyond it was a square of morning sky, clear and warm and richly blue. As she watched, a white risen cloud edged across one corner of it, a sparrow came and perched upon the sill, seeking vainly for such morsels as sometimes awaited him there. She gazed upon the bird with recognition, smiling.

"You shall have your crumbs, little one," she said, speaking aloud, and thus rose to begin the untried day.

The house was a single room, sparingly furnished with low seats and benches, tables, chests. A wall niche held a lamp from the Street of Potters, the flaxen wick floating in oil from the olive grove, kindled at nightfall to give forth a wavering radiance. On a shelf near the large table were the utensils of the household. At the doorway stood two red clay jars, filled with water during the hours of day but now, in the early morning, near to empty. Against the wall was the wedding chest of Anne in which had been laid those things dear to her heart, among

2

them the family scrolls which showed her to be of the House of David, descended from David the King, as was her husband.

The people of David, being nomads in this land, had followed the grazing herds and flocks, and dwelt in tents. It had been a custom among them to have a portion of each tent set aside for the women, curtained by a heavy woven drapery, a hanging rug. And even though that day was many generations past, the custom remained, and thus, in the House in Nazareth, Mary possessed a curtained space of her own, as did Anne, her mother. It was in these small rooms, contrived each night, that they spread their bed mats. Here they slept and woke and bathed and took up their clothing, and kept the little portion of things to be called their own. Here Mary could look upon all she possessed, a small earthen water jar, a simple clay lamp, the loom for her weaving, the chest which held her garments and certain small treasures.

Standing in a shaft of light from the risen sun, she washed with water from the jar, combed out her soft dark hair, put on her straight, homespun dress and girded it at the waist. Then, rolling up the bed mat, she placed it neatly upon the wall shelf near the lamp, and put aside the curtain of her seclusion.

Moving softly, she went to stand for a moment in the open doorway of her mother's house which, like other houses of Nazareth, was small and square, wrought of plaster-sheathed stone, with a low ceiling of cypress beams. A small outer stair led to the flat rooftop which served as the common room of the family, being a pleasing place for rest, for prayer, for quiet talk, for seeking the cool winds which sprang up at sunset. And, in the heat of noontide, it was well chosen for the drying of herbs, of fruit or cheese, flax or newly washed linens.

Behind the house was a court enclosed in a stone wall, high and of stalwart thickness. Within it were a few ewes and lambs, a hen with her chicks, a small and shaggy donkey. The

3

broad and sheltering leaves of a fig tree spared them from the burning of the sun, the falling dew, the lashing rains of winter. Beyond, in another portion of the court, it spread a pattern of light and shadow upon the wall, shading the corner where the beehive-shaped oven awaited the baking of the daily bread.

A night mist had come upon the countryside, white as a cloud. Now, as the long yellow rays of sunlight parted it, it thinned and began to drift away. Everything was drenched in dew, the trees, the garden, the flowers opening in tall grasses, the caravan road beyond the village, the shrubs of the hillside, the fertile valley below. And now, in the strengthening radiance, the village stirred and was restored to life. Smoke from the early fires drifted from open doorways, blue and thin and fragrant on the cool morning air. There came to Mary from beyond the wall the voices of men setting forth to market, their footfalls thudding softly in the dampened street. A woman passed, trudging toward the well, humming a tuneless, meditative song. In the distance, a child wept fretfully.

Suddenly the harsh, insistent braying of the donkey roused her to remembrance of his need, and she hastened into the court, that she might tend him. It was the way of every worthy household. A man, arising from sleep, must think first of God, then of the seeking and thirsting animals in his care. Afterward, he might ease his own hunger, but no just man would sit at meat while his animals knew want.

She bore an armful of hay to the donkey and stood for a moment beside him, stroking his shaggy head. Then, when she had turned from him, she scattered grain to the hen and chicks, calling them lightly. Afterward, she filled the stone trough with water for the flock, lingering to caress the fleecy backs of the ewes, to take up and fondle the smallest of the lambs. When they had done with drinking, she led them into the street now hot with yellow sunlight, dried to feathery dust. They went forth hurriedly to the pasture just beyond the

4

village. It was a common pasture used by a number of families, their cattle and sheep and goats driven to it daily and tended by a shepherd in the hire of all.

Returning, she went within the house, concerned for her mother who, of late, had appeared both frail and ill. Yet on this morning, Anne had prevailed against the weakness which sometimes afflicted her, had come forth clad in her simple homespun dress, with a length of wool folded about her spare shoulders, against the early chill.

"How is it with my dear one this day?" and Anne embraced the girl with utter tenderness.

She had been past the days of her youth when Mary was born to her, and now had come to the latter season of her life. Her face was deeply patterned with all that she had known of living, with compassion and sorrow, with sudden small lines of merriment and rejoicing, with the quiet, kindly judgment which looked forth from her eyes. Her veined hands were seared and roughened by a lifetime of unsparing toil, yet tenderness rose within all who beheld them thus, recalling the numberless times when she had lifted up the newborn, brought peace to the dying, sheltered the fatherless, given meat to those who hungered. Indeed, there was no woman in Nazareth more beloved for the immeasurable strength of her wisdom, the simple goodness of her pious heart.

Now, as on every morning, since hers was a Jewish household, she turned to the first duty of the day: the reading of a verse from the holy writings, the lifting of the spirit to God. And, in truth, Mary would cherish no dearer memory of her girlhood than the stillness within the dimly lighted room where she and her mother lingered in the silence of prayer, a shaft of sunlight falling upon the doorsill, the fragrance of wood smoke borne on the light wind of morning, the distant calling of doves, the sweet and gentle voice of Anne lifted in the imperishable words of their faith, *"Lord, thou hast been our dwelling place in all generations...."*

Afterward, when she and her mother had broken the morning bread together, Mary took up one of the clay water jars and set out for the well. It was indeed a place blessed by God, where living water poured forth by day and by night, where countless travelers halted to quench the thirst upon them, to fill their goatskin bottles, where at morning and evening, came the women and girls of the village, bearing their pitchers and jars.

The cool sweetness of dew and morning mist had vanished, borne on the wind, the rays of the strengthening sun. Children ran to their play, old men sat dreaming upon their doorsills, lads set out, with slow and reluctant steps, to the lessons of the law. Flocks of sheep were driven to the common pasture in clouds of reddened dust, and flocks of goats also. Women set their pitchers upon their shoulders and went forth from their houses in the sun. Winged creatures set up a clamorous singing in the trees.

A faint gleam of sweat moistened Mary's smooth forehead and the dust was hot beneath her small feet, scorching the bare soles. She turned, at length, into another street and, after the way of many daughters of Nazareth, glanced swiftly, secretly toward the home of Joseph, the young carpenter. And when she perceived that he stood in the doorway of his shop, her heart quickened within her breast, a sweet confusion came upon her. She cast her eyes downward, hastily and with seemliness, nor did she lift them toward him again, yet she knew he gazed upon her as she passed, and the thought filled her with a tremulous happiness.

Within every village there was at least one carpenter who worked with uncommon skill in some humble little shop, dealing with sound and seasoned wood, planing and sawing it, forming it in useful, sometimes beautiful ways. By his hand

6

were fashioned yokes for the oxen, benches, beds, axe handles, wheels, cradles, wedding chests, and many more things concerned with the common striving of all, with households and with trade, with toil and rest and worship, marriage and birth, even with death. Thus every man in the village had need of him, visited him often, spoke with him day upon day, so that he was known to them utterly, his thoughts, his virtues, his weaknesses. In such a manner was Joseph known, yet there was none who had as much as a single word to bring forth against him.

Joseph had come to Nazareth after the death of the old carpenter, who had been his kinsman and the last of his mother's family. From that day forward, the girls of the village had looked upon him with yearning, seeing that he was young and lean and well-favored beyond others known to them. In truth, he was tall, with broadly muscled shoulders and arms, with thick dark hair, a beard neatly trimmed to his jawline, mouth and eyes that could smile together in great gentleness and good humor. And those who passed his shop after the setting of the sun, when he had ended the work of the day, perceived how it was that he studied the holy writings, seated at his table, bent close to the wavering lamp.

Joseph had dwelt within the village less than a year, yet with word that he was unwed, he had brought upon himself the dreams of the unbetrothed, the risen hopes of many mothers, the searching eyes of all the elders. It was not good that a man should live alone, they declared. Nay, he was in need of a worthy wife for the baking of his bread, the tending of his house and garden, the bearing of his sons. And, now that Joseph had passed his twentieth year, surely the time had come for such a choice to be brought about. Even Joseph said as much, revealing how his coming to Nazareth had been also the seeking of a wife. For within his own village, a distant place of few families, none had laid hold upon his heart.

7

In truth, he was of Mary's own blood, for he belonged, as did her parents, to the House of David. And, as all men knew, it was a seemly thing that kinsmen should dwell together in marriage. Yet he had spoken no word before her father, and now there remained to her no near male relative beyond Cleophas, who had wed her kinswoman. Still, she thought shyly, it may be that he will one day go forth to Cleophas. . . .

She went on down the street, hastening a little now since she had passed the shop of the young carpenter so slowly, returning to thought of the tasks awaiting her. From season to season, from year to year, her small hands seemed overflowing with toil. She planted and tended the vegetables of the garden, labored with the harvesting of fruit and grain, pressed olives for the lamps and for the jars stored against need, dealt with spindle and with loom, tended the animals, sought brushwood for the supper fires, gathered and dried herbs and flax and fruit, washed the linens, made ready the foods of the table, ground the meal and baked the daily bread, bore water from the well, helped with those of the village who suffered illness and want.

Already a dozen women were gathered at the well, each awaiting her turn, giving the moments to talk and laughter, their voices as light as the twittering of birds. Some, younger yet than Mary, held children of their own flesh in their arms. They called to her with affection, and when she had taken her place among them, she put down her water jar for a little time, that she might know their companionship.

It came to her then that there was an uncommon excitement upon them, and upon the unwed girls who gathered with them. Jerusha, Susanna, Judith, Rebecca. . . . Yet it was Susanna, a merry-hearted and audacious girl with flashing black eyes and curled black hair, who rejoiced among them. And after a little time, the cause was made known.

8

"Joseph, the carpenter, has sent word that he desires to speak with her father at nightfall. . . ."

For a moment, Mary was stunned beyond utterance. In truth, she thought dully, he has chosen his betrothed. And such misery assailed her that the radiance of the morning was shattered before her eyes. Afterward she strove to recall what it was that she had said before them, some kindly word, graciously spoken for the sake of Susanna, who was beloved in the eyes of all the village. Yet she could bear to linger among them no longer and, having filled the clay jar, hastened from them, heart-stricken by that which she had heard.

At the doorway of her mother's house, she set the jar in shadow, covering it with green leaves freshly plucked, that the coolness might remain with it. Then, going within the garden, she knelt among the plants and began the task of weeding, tearing the unwanted growths from the soil as she yearned to tear the wretchedness from her own heart. Yet such a sense of loneliness and sorrow assailed her that she was unable to prevail against it. It was as though his name was uttered, again and again within her thoughts: Joseph, Joseph. . . . And such desolation was upon her as she had not known before this hour.

9

II.

THE PROVINCE OF GALILEE WAS NOT UNLIKE A GARDEN YIELDING rich and bountiful harvests. Thus there were many within it who tilled the land, yet they did not remain apart in lonely dwellings easily plundered by any passing highwayman, but were gathered together in clustered villages.

All manner of evil followed the great roads of trade, and who was to say when a man might require the protection of his neighbors? In truth, it was so, even of Nazareth, for numberless strangers traveled the broad caravan way just beyond its walls.

These, beholding the quiet village, gazed upon its simplicity with worldly arrogance, and uttered many a jest concerning it: "Can anything good come out of Nazareth?"

Yet the beauty of Galilee was known abroad, and tales of its fruitfulness borne far beyond its borders by caravan leaders, and others of the highroads. Within Galilee, they declared, one beheld all manner of flowering shrubs and magnificent trees, gazed upon the cloudy groves of olives, the patterns of ripened vineyards, the sown fields, and white, orderly settlements. And there was, likewise, the Sea of Galilee, a lake of such immeasurable loveliness that it was said to be chosen of the Lord.

Nazareth was set high among the hills in a shallow green basin that opened to the south, so that those who dwelt within it might gaze, unperceived, upon the travelers on the great plain of Esdraelon below. From the summit of the slope to which the village clung, it was possible to behold as much as half the land of Palestine. Toward the north rose hills blue with distance, and the white and shining summit of Hermon, mount of eternal snows from which fertility streamed unceasingly upon the land. To the east lay the blue loveliness of the lake and below it, the Jordan River, crawling like a serpent through a tangled growth of creepers, shrubs, and trees, making its way to a desolate valley of sand and shale. Westward, one beheld the gleaming waters of the great sea which stretched even to Rome.

In Nazareth, Mary had been born and would be content to die, for life within its walls was a matter known and understood. A day was not unlike the day before it, nor the day which came after. The sun rose through wet leaves and mist, strengthened and burned, so that, by midday, many of the village went within their doors, seeking refuge from the merciless heat, resting from the labors of the morning, sleeping for a little time. Trees and shrubs and vines brought forth sweet and cooling shade, gardens and vineyards ripened, flowers came into bloom, flocks brought forth young, olives and apricots and pomegranates grew round upon the branches. Babes were born, wept and grew to a hardy youth; then aged and sickened and died and were borne to their tombs. There were neighbors both diligent and slothful, virtuous and evil, sound and infirm, in the spring and winter seasons of their years. It was like any small village anywhere, since the first small village was wrought by the hand of the Lord. And there were many born in Nazareth who died without ever departing from it, save for the pious duty of making a holy pilgrimage to Jerusalem.

Mary knew but little of the world beyond Nazareth, and had no yearning to go forth to it. In truth, she yearned only

11

for the sweet obscurity of becoming wife to Joseph the carpenter, dwelling within a house fashioned by his own strength and skill, tending his hearth fires, bearing his sons. At the holy season of the Passover, she had gone up to Jerusalem with her parents. Yet she was both troubled and disquieted by the thronged streets of the great city, the cold faces of the imperious nobles, the unceasing tread of Roman soldiers passing with arrogance before the humble Jews. It was a pleasing thing to turn again to Nazareth, to enter the cool dimness of the small, familiar house, dwell in the love of the Lord and of her kinsmen.

Throughout the land, the ties of family were of such strength that good fortune befalling one member meant good fortune for all, the same being true of sorrow or shame. In the manner of the East, all maids and women within a family were said to be sisters, all men and lads known as brothers, even though uncles, cousins, nieces, or brothers-in-law were to be counted among them. Thus a stranger might dwell for months within the gates before their true kinship was known and understood in his eyes.

In another street, a little distance away, dwelt Cleophas, a man quiet, just, even-handed, named head of their family since the death of Mary's father. His wife, called Mary Cleophas, that she might be known from other women of the village who shared her given name, was a kinswoman of kindliness and diligence, quick of tongue, merry of spirit. And by reason of her unceasing generosity of heart, she came each day to the house of Anne, that she might know how they fared, for it was a sad thing to be fatherless, or a widow. Had they meal and oil in plenty? And what of the eggs, the fruits newly plucked from the branch, the vegetables still wet with the dews of the garden? Would they not have Cleophas bear a basket of these to market in one of the neighboring towns when he went forth to the selling of his own? For Mary Cleo-

12

phas desired both joy and prosperity for those near to her heart.

A day's journey to the north was the city of Capernaum, on the beautiful lake of Galilee. Here also dwelt a kinswoman of Mary, the cheerful and hearty Salome, whom she saw only at the season of the Passover. Though but a year older than Mary, Salome had been three years wed to a young fisherman, Zebedee, and since he was a man of wealth, they dwelt in a fair stone house with a servant at their command.

There were likewise some cousins in the small village of Cana, a little way to the north.

Yet the kinswoman most dearly beloved in the heart of Mary dwelt so vast a distance to the south that they met but seldom . . . Elizabeth, the cousin who was not unlike some spirit of goodness fair to behold, ever to be remembered. And, in truth, she possessed an uncommon beauty, being tall and gracefully formed, gentle of manner and voice, with a face of utter saintliness.

Elizabeth was the wife of Zacharias, a priest of great virtue, and dwelt with him in the village of Ain Karim, a little distance south of Jerusalem, where her husband served the crumbling synagogue. And truly, it was a village of wretched poverty, yet those who dwelt within it were without discontent, being blessed of the Lord.

Having been born many years earlier than Mary, Elizabeth was as an elder sister in her eyes. Long before, when she and her husband had dwelt in Nazareth, she had often borne the child Mary within her own house, had been both merry and tender with her, kneaded small honey cakes for her delight, joined her in endless pretenses of spinning and weaving, the plucking of fruit, the grinding of flour. And Zacharias also had known pleasure in the little one. Thus he took her for walks in the hills, told her numberless stories, delighted her with riddles. Indeed, he and Elizabeth loved her as though she

13

had been a child of their own flesh; and they had no other, seeing that neither sons nor daughters had been born to them.

Yet throughout the years, Elizabeth had told her, speaking out of a serene and unfaltering faith, "God will send us a child in His own time, for He has heard our prayers."

Save for Jerusalem, city of Jewish worship, and the towns which sheltered her brethren, Mary knew little of the world beyond her doorsill. She could not say how it was that the forces of Caesar had come to rule the world, even the province of Galilee. At some time beyond the reaches of her memory, Rome had conquered the Jewish people and set above them an alien king, the barbaric and evil Herod.

Like other women of Nazareth, Mary understood that in the vast, unfathomed distance across the western sea dwelt the emperor Tiberius, the Roman ruler to whom tribute must be paid even though a man's children perished for want of bread . . . Tiberius, whose name must not be spoken without honor, lest the speaker be charged with treason and brought to his own death. Beyond this, Mary knew nothing, save that the Romans were among the ungodly, and had rendered her people defenseless within their own land.

For uncounted years, they had known the unsparing cruelty of Herod, the merciless oppression of Rome. At times, certain Jews had risen against the injustices inflicted upon them, with bitter and unavailing defiance. By Roman might such rebellions were put down as quickly as a mighty storm would quench a candle. Those numbered among the rebels were brought to death, their homes assailed and burned, their families tortured, slain, or seized as slaves. Hundreds were crucified in the degrading and horrifying Roman death, nailed to high crosses and left to die in unutterable anguish beneath the burning heat of the sun. In truth, none could say how many Jewish people had been slain.

Nor did a man dare lift his voice against such terrors, for

14

the spies of Herod were everywhere, and Roman garrisons established in the land. At times, when she gathered plants and herbs in the hills, Mary would gaze across at the high-road, and watch the passing of a Roman legion. They were magnificently trained soldiers who moved with masterly perfection, their shields and helmets shining in the sun. At their head, on a gleaming black horse, rode their leader, a centurion. Above them flashed the dread emblem of Roman ruthlessness and might, the golden eagle. It was a splendid yet terrifying sight, and the heart of Mary was quickened in her bosom, even as the hearts of all others who looked upon it. For it seemed to the Jews that the tireless and unsparing feet of the Romans were trampling their very lives into the dust.

Yet there remained within them a single radiant hope whispered from generation to generation, echoed daily by the lips of their priests and teachers, and in their holy writings. A Savior, a Messiah, a king greater than Herod, more powerful than Tiberius Caesar, one anointed of the Lord, would be sent to spare them, to drive forth their conquerors, to lift the burden of suffering from them, restore justice and mercy to the land, and to their lives.

Throughout Jewish history there had risen prophets to whom it was given to hear the voice of the Lord, whose words, therefore, were inscribed upon scrolls that they might be cherished, read, and remembered. Thus the Jewish people had besought their priests to repeat for them, again and again, the syllables of prophecy which dealt with the coming of the Savior.

As a child, Mary had heard these words from the lips of her parents and kinsmen, in the whisperings of village children whose surmises were beyond probability, but pleasing to dwell upon. The Messiah, said the lads of Nazareth, would march upon Jerusalem with the sound of many trumpets and the mighty noise of war, so that the Romans, assailed by terror, would flee from the city and destroy themselves in the waters of the western sea.

But Zacharias spoke otherwise.

"We know not the manner of his coming, neither the day nor the hour. Yet the prophets have told many things concerning him. In the time set by the Lord, they will come to pass. . . ."

And he repeated the words of the scrolls.

The Messiah would be born of a virgin mother in the little town of Bethlehem, and would belong to the royal House of David. He would possess the spirit of wisdom and understanding, of counsel and might. He would give sight to the blind, comfort the sorrowing, bring light into darkness. He would magnify the law and make it honorable and bring forth judgment to the Gentiles. A voice crying in the wilderness would tell of his coming.

And there was yet more spoken by the lips of the prophets. He would come before them humbly, riding upon a donkey, and would be hailed in the manner of a king. Yet many would turn their faces from him, so that he would be despised and rejected, a man of sorrows acquainted with grief. He would be sold for thirty pieces of silver. He would be led like a lamb to the slaughter and, like a sheep before the shearers, would utter no protest. His hands and feet would be pierced, he would be sorely treated, taken from prison and judgment, and slain for the sins of his people. His garments would be divided among his enemies, who would cast lots for them. And when he died, he would make his grave with the wicked and the rich. Yet, of the increase of his government and peace, there would be no end.

All these things and more had been inscribed upon the scrolls in the words of Jewish prophets who had heard the voice of the Lord. All these things and more Zacharias and

Elizabeth had revealed to the wondering child, while the moon shone down upon the village streets, even as now.

For the disquieted day had come to an end, and though Mary concealed it from the eyes of her mother, the silence of dusk had afflicted her with even greater heaviness of heart. Soon after the breaking of the evening bread, Cleophas had knocked at their doorposts, desiring to confer with Anne. Seeing that he spoke in grave tones, as though he would not be overheard, Mary went quietly from the room, and up to the coolness of the rooftop.

Now, in silence and solitude, she gazed beyond the moonlit streets, out into the darkened hills beyond. The shop of Joseph was closed, without light. And suddenly Mary thought of Elizabeth with an anguish of yearning, recalling how it was that her cousin had comforted her sorrows in all the years of her growing up. Yes, truly, even this sorrow would be lessened, could she but reveal to Elizabeth how it was that Joseph, the carpenter, had turned not to her, but to another, and had shattered the heart within her breast.

Yet who could say when she and Elizabeth would meet again? The distance from Nazareth to Ain Karim was the space of a long journey, even for tidings borne from mouth to mouth. At times, some neighbor of Nazareth set forth on a journey of trade to Cana or Jerusalem or Capernaum, and returned bearing word of her kinsmen. Thus she had learned in the days of early autumn, a length of six months before, that Zacharias had gone up to Jerusalem to serve in the great temple. For Zacharias, as for many priests, this was a duty performed once each year.

Before the coming of the winter rains, autumn was a season of unsparing heat when the earth lay cracked and scorched, and many wells were empty. Surely the road to Jerusalem had been choked with dust, and burning hot beneath the sun.

She thought of Elizabeth watching from the Court of

17

Women in the great temple, of Zacharias, in his white robe, casting incense upon the fire of the golden altar. The incense, being of powdered spices and flowers, would burn with a sweet fragrance, sending up clouds of thin white smoke. Whereupon all those who watched would pray in silence and with humble hearts, saying to themselves, "Like the smoke of the incense, my prayer is rising up to God." And from Zacharias also would rise a prayer yet unfulfilled, a prayer for the blessing of a son.

Suddenly, Mary became aware that Cleophas had gone forth from the house, and her mother was calling her name. She rose quickly from her seat on the low balustrade and hastened down the steps, seeing at once that some uncommon thing had come to pass. Anne's withered cheeks were flushed, her voice trembling.

"Cleophas . . ." she stammered, then. "Word he brought that there is one . . . of character and family . . . who would make you his wife. . . ."

Mary drew away, assailed by dismay. Yes, truly, it was seemly that a man desiring to become her husband should seek the consent of Cleophas, yet . . .

The eyes of Anne were radiant with joy.

"Now surely the Lord has heard me! For he is such a man as I have prayed your husband might be, humble yet wise, strong yet kind, and also of the House of David."

Mary's lips were dry, her heart as cold as a stone.

"Who . . . who is he?" she whispered.

"Joseph the carpenter."

"*Joseph!*" the cry was one of utter astonishment.

"Surely he is known to you," pleaded Anne. "Surely you have looked upon him, passing his shop. . . ."

Not once did it come to me, thought Mary, astonished, that he might desire to see the father of Susanna on some matter of trade. . . .

And now Anne's face was filled with anxiety.

"Surely . . ." she said again.

Whereupon Mary cast herself into her mother's arms.

"Have no fear!" she cried, and her voice was filled with rejoicing, and with bright young laughter.

III

III.

THE DAY HAD COME TO AN END, AND THE FAMILIAR SOUNDS OF early evening fell softly upon Mary's ears as she lingered, wearied by her labors, in the cool shadow of the arbor, where grape leaves stirred in the freshened wind borne in upon the village at the setting of the sun. It was a pleasing place in which to ponder all that had come to pass, to deal with thoughts of Joseph, with remembrance of her betrothal, with dreams of her wedding day.

A promise of marriage was a solemn matter and not to be concealed, but to be told abroad. Thus if any had cause to think it ill-advised, he must consider it a matter of both duty and conscience to speak before the contract of betrothal was written.

When Cleophas first brought Joseph within the house, Mary perceived with what care the young carpenter had washed and garbed himself, saw that he possessed a quiet dignity, and knew a timid pride in him. She, herself, had been seated between Anne and Mary Cleophas, appearing small and young and shy. Her hands were folded together, her eyes lowered, so that her lashes cast half-moon shadows upon the apricot tint of her cheeks, and her soft dark hair was yet another shadow falling upon her white-clad shoulders. Indeed, it was known to her that Joseph's first visit would be courteously remote, and any words which they might speak together

20

would be akin to the words of strangers who did not think to meet again. It was the custom of the land, and therefore not to be disdained. Yet when the glance of Joseph met her own, she read in his dark eyes the gentle words: *Have no fear of me, Mary . . . for I will be a good husband to you all my days.* Whereupon her own eyes answered: *I am not afraid, beloved. It is my wish to be your wife.*

Still, as the elders counseled, such a choice was not to be made in haste, and thus the winter passed, and spring came to the hills of Galilee before the writing of a marriage contract between Joseph, the carpenter, and Mary, daughter of Anne, wife of Joachim.

The day was clamorous with preparations, both house and courtyard being thronged with women who dealt with the grinding of meal, the kneading of bread, the baking of sweet-meats and honey cakes. Bowls and platters were filled with figs and almonds, olives and honey. The table was spread with richly ripened fruits and newly plucked vegetables, with cheese and milk, with the grape and nut wines borne forth on the days of espousals and weddings. Gladly, and with open hearts, those of the village brought the loveliest fruits of their gardens, their new-laid eggs, even some fowls for the roasting.

It was forbidden that Mary put her hand to the smallest task on this festive day. In the last hour of the afternoon, she garbed herself in a soft white tunic, girded by a length of blue embroidered linen, and sandals with needle-wrought designs from the hand of her mother. Then, being summoned by the hearty voice of Mary Cleophas, she went forth to receive the white betrothal wreath of blossoms gathered by the village girls. Even Susanna came to wish her well, nor did the girl sorrow after Joseph, having turned her fancy to another.

Mary recalled how it was that, for the first time, she and Joseph had sat together at the head of the table, awaiting their guests. These came at the going down of the sun, neighbors and companions of many seasons, each bearing a gift for her who was to be a bride. It was only after the last had entered and had been seated, each in his own place, that the rabbi rose to deal with the matter of the marriage pledge. Then Joseph rose also and, with quiet dignity, laid forth such betrothal money as the law required of him, and certain gifts for those of Mary's family. Afterward, he handed one of his sandals to the rabbi who, in turn, placed it in the hands of Mary. It was the custom, long honored in the land, of sealing a bargain, of binding a promise. And when he had brought forth the contract, two of the company set their hands to it, as witnesses.

Then, seeing that the rites of espousal were ended, the company turned to feasting and wine, and were merry until the risen moon was half across the sky.

Afterward, Joseph lingered until all other guests had departed, and when she had bidden him good night, Mary's fingers clung for a moment to the warmth and tenderness of his hand. With the coming of summer, the rites of their marriage would be held, yet until that time she would see him only rarely, after the custom of the village. She stood silent in the doorway, watching him stride down the street in the white radiance of the full moon which brought good fortune to those espoused within its rays. And not until he had vanished within the shadows did she turn again to the house.

Since then another day had dawned, another sun was setting in the waters of the Great Sea to the west. Anne was breaking the evening bread in the house of Mary Cleophas, and Mary was alone beneath the darkening shelter of leaves and vines. Along the street was wafted the pleasant smell of the supper fires. The light twittering of nesting birds sounded from the olive trees. The sheep and lambs, driven hurriedly from pasture by a hungry shepherd lad, flocked into the courtyard, the ewes settling against the wall with their little ones close beside them. The hen tucked her chicks beneath her broad wings and

22

presently slept. Even the little donkey closed his long-lashed eyes and dozed in the last rays of the declining sun.

Suddenly aware of the hour, Mary recalled that she must once more go forth to the well. Thus she rose and went within the house for one of the red clay jars, and hastened along the empty street bearing it upon her shoulder. The shop of Joseph was dark, save for a single lamp gleaming from the small back room where he slept and took his meals. She lingered a moment before it, yearning to cross the street and make her way within the open door and call to him.

"Joseph, it is I. All day my thoughts have turned to you. . . ."

Yet a flush of shame came upon her when she considered the bold and unmaidenly sound of the words. Thus she put the yearning from her and hastened forth along the street, leaving light, quick footprints in the soft yellow dust, making no sound.

It was not to be believed that the well was deserted. Yet there was beside it no gathering of travelers, neither women of the village nor their children, no voices lifted in light-hearted welcome: "Hail, Mary! Only see the new tooth of my little one. . . ." There was not as much as a passing lad, stooping to quench his thirst with a dripping handful of water from the ancient stone trough, not even a dog of the streets, or a cricket chirping in the dampness.

Then the village was darkened suddenly by the swift purple dusk of lands to the east, and it came to Mary that an uncommon stillness hovered about her, a silence in which she heard not even the flutter of a wing, the trembling of a leaf. Bewildered, she set the pitcher upon the stones of the well and stood, unmoving, beside it, her lips parted by the measure of her wonder, taut with listening.

And a quiet voice was lifted against the soundless night.

"Hail, Mary. . . ."

23

She started and, turning, gazed swiftly about her. Yet she was utterly alone. And now, it appeared to her that there had fallen upon all the earth a stillness not unlike the hush of waiting, the silence of prayer.

Frightened, she made haste to fill the water jar, and turned homeward, moving hurriedly, fearfully, her small feet pattering in the shadowy dust beneath the trees. There was no one to be seen. The streets were wholly emptied, the doorsills vacant, the windows dim. And the same silence was upon her mother's house, and upon the courtyard where not a leaf of the olive tree stirred, not a bough moved in the wind. The hen and the animals slept, indistinct shapes of quiet breathing in the gloom.

Yet when she had entered her own doorway, she ceased to be disquieted, and her breath came evenly, without haste. She set the filled water jar upon the swept floor and reached for the lamp. Then a heart-sinking fear came upon her. She had perceived no movement, heard no sound, yet it was known to her that another stood within the room. She could feel, in the dimness, another presence, as though eyes watched upon her, a hand was stretched forth to lay its touch upon her. Then out of the silence and darkness rose the quiet voice that had come to her at the well.

"Hail, full of grace. The Lord is with you. Blessed are you among women. . . ."

A mist of light welled up into the room. The girl turned, stricken with terror. The radiance strengthened, turned to golden light, and within it there stood, quietly, with lifted head and folded hands, one with a holy countenance, like the faces of the young priests who sometimes came to speak with Zacharias. Yet it was known to her that he was not of this world. And even as she would have fled from him, driven by unreasoning panic, he spoke again, in tones of gentle understanding.

24

"Do not be afraid, Mary, for you have found favor with God."

Then the silence returned and, with it, a sense of refuge, as though she knew herself shielded, protected, blessed. Her body ceased its trembling, the terror departed from her eyes, so that she listened without fear to that which he would have her know.

"And behold . . . you shall bring forth a son, and shall call his name Jesus . . . and he shall reign over the House of Jacob forever, and of his kingdom there shall be no end."

"How . . . how shall this be," the girl faltered, then, "seeing that I know not a man?"

And he said to her, "The Holy Spirit will come upon you, and the power of the Most High will overshadow you, and the holy one to be born of you shall be called the Son of God."

And there was more that he told her, saying that Elizabeth, the beloved cousin, she who was called barren, would bring forth a child of her own when three moons had come to pass.

Whereupon Mary stared at him, striving against her own unbelief. She, Mary of Nazareth, who knew not a man, to bring forth a son. . . . Elizabeth and Zacharias to receive the child of their prayers after barren and fruitless years. . . . And, knowing what doubts assailed her, he spoke again, reminding her of that which, for the space of a moment, she had ceased to remember.

"For nothing is impossible with God."

The quiet words rebuked her. Thus she lifted her eyes and answered in a voice strengthened by faith and humility and utter trust, "I am the handmaiden of the Lord. Let it be done to me according to your word."

And the messenger of God departed from her.

For a time she stood wordless and alone, dazed with wonder. It came to her then that the village was no longer silent. Sounds familiar to her ears through all the years of her growing up

25

arose now to reassure her. She heard the murmurous voices of men who had halted that they might speak together, the footfalls of a donkey ridden through the dust, a child's laugh. Wind stirred the boughs of the olive tree, a bird called from its nest in the hedge, and one of the lambs cried out plaintively, as if it dreamed.

Slowly, she kindled the lamp and, lifting it, gazed upon that which was before her. All that stood within the room came into being before the yellow flame, the table, the benches, the burnished jars and bowls, the wedding chest of Anne, and there was no wonder in the sight. Had she indeed beheld a messenger of God within this unchanged room and heard from his lips the words of a prophecy?

Suddenly, she longed to turn from the house and run through the streets in the light of the risen moon, to knock on the doors of Joseph's shop, now closed against the night, and reveal to him all that had come to pass. Yet there was a certain question not to be answered. Would Joseph believe her words?

She put the lamp down quietly, and stood staring into the flame, her hands tightened, one upon the other, an anguish of uncertainty upon her. Would anyone believe her words? And now the lined and beloved face of Anne came before her, twisted by grief. She saw Cleophas, drawing away from her, conferring hastily with his wife, gazing upon her with unconcealed suspicion. Those of the village, the elders, the rabbi, the women who had kneaded the bread of her betrothal feast, the girls who had gathered the fair white flowers . . . in truth, it was as though they stood before her, staring upon her, whispering together, scorning her name.

Nay, this matter was not to be revealed to her mother, seeing that Anne might suffer grief because of it . . . not to Mary Cleophas, lest she turn upon Joseph with bitter and accusing words . . . nor yet to any maids of her own years, since it was

26

beyond their understanding. Yet a face lovely in its serenity rose before her eyes . . . the wise and untroubled and blessed Elizabeth.

Cleophas was to depart for Jerusalem at daylight, bearing the goods of the village craftsmen to the great market. Surely it would not appear unseemly that she should go forth to the house of her cousin while her mother lingered with Mary Cleophas, while she might travel in the protection of him who was her guardian. Thus she went to a certain chest and brought from it a tablet and stylus, that she might begin the writing of the letter she would leave behind.

IV.

THEY JOURNEYED UP TO JERUSALEM WITH A SMALL CARAVAN of traders, the kindly, stolid Cleophas and Mary, the young and troubled girl.

The three provinces of Palestine rose, one above the other, Judea, Samaria, Galilee, the last being far to the north. The holy city of Jerusalem lay in Judea, to the south, yet travelers seldom crossed Samaria to reach it, seeing that in the eyes of the Samaritans all Jews were despised. Thus it was a matter of prudence for lone travelers, even small caravans, to seek the lengthier way, southward along the river Jordan to the city of Jericho, and thence westward to Jerusalem, through the desolate wilderness which lay between. Nor was this road unfamiliar to those of Galilee, being the same which may had taken on their way to the feast of the Passover.

For a time the caravan traveled through the loveliness of Galilee, the rich gardens, the ripening fields. Later, they turned southward along the Jordan, through blossoming shrubs and spreading trees, and tall green stems of oleander burdened with bloom.

Yet, a little time later, the Jordan ceased to be a stream consoling and benevolent, and became a black serpent in a region of destruction. Here were marshlands heavy with slime, tangled with dead and barren trees, with broken roots and dark thickets which gave shelter to vipers and howling beasts

28

and savage birds of prey. It was a place terrifying to look upon, and those of the caravan quickened their steps as they beheld it.

The journey, being three days in length, was a wearisome thing, assailed during the hours of daylight by heat and flies and wretchedness. At night, the travelers shivered within their cloaks and crept near to the warmth of their fires, or of their animals. Yet there was among them a Teller of Tales, a man white of hair and beard who would sit before the gates of Jerusalem and reveal wonders for a few coins tossed into his reaching, unwashed hands. And the journey was made less burdensome by reason of the tales from his lips.

On a certain afternoon, he told of the Essenes, an order of Jewish monks who dwelt upon the shores of the Dead Sea nearby in utter poverty, desiring no portion of the world's riches or ease or merriment, striving only for unity with God. In the holiest of vows, they had declared before the Lord that they would live forever in justice and mercy, hatred of evil, love of truth, reproof of liars, compassion toward one another, turning neither in anger nor in vengeance upon any man.

Afterward, they were baptized with the Waters of Purification, yet it was said that, even so, they would not be cleansed unless they had turned from their iniquity and become unblemished of heart. Holiness, they declared, was more pleasing to God than the flesh of burnt offerings, the sound of pious words.

The monks did not marry, but often received into their community lads whose parents had died, that these might become even as themselves. Thus they dwelt together in unbelievable austerity, with prayer and silence and the searching of the scriptures, wresting a bare existence from the miserable soil.

"For it is foretold," said the Teller of Tales, "that they will prepare the way of the Messiah, who is to come."

29

And hearing these words, Mary's heart was set to trembling. How is it, she asked herself again, that I am chosen of the Lord?

They did not linger in Jericho, though it was a city of great loveliness, of shadowed streets and cool springs, of stirred palm fronds and numberless blossoms. Here stood the palaces of kings, the high houses of Roman nobles, and of the wealthy Jews who had made the Romans their friends. And some of the caravan spat in the dust before these houses, despising those who would turn their backs upon their own people for the sake of gain, departing from the paths of the Lord.

Afterward, they had trudged across the vast and burning desert wilderness where Mary's little donkey clambered among the rocks, trembling as his hoofs slipped at the edge of a steep and narrow trail above a shadowed gorge. Knowing his terror, Mary leaned forward and spoke to him, comforting his fears with the sound of her voice, the gentle touch of her hand.

"Have courage, little one," she said quietly. "It is but a little distance more. . . ."

About them lay the vast wilderness of Judah, a stony desert of waiting silences and immeasurable desolation. One looked upon endless hills barren of either trees or scrub, parched by the suns of numberless centuries. One passed the ghostly remains of cities long fallen to the dust, the tales of their glory lost in time, to be found neither upon the tongues of men, nor upon the scrolls of their fathers. In all this wild loneliness there was no sound save the whisper of sand against stone, nothing of life save a single vulture which moved slowly above the caravan, its shadow hovering upon the trodden way before them.

Through the wretchedness of unrelenting heat, they began the long ascent toward Jerusalem, clambering upward and upward until suddenly, the holy city was revealed to their eyes, and they beheld the golden temple gleaming in the sun.

It was a sight which had stirred uncounted Jewish hearts, restored many a strengthless spirit, quickened many a faltering step.

And now, according to his counsel, Mary parted from Cleophas. Among those of the caravan were a certain joiner and his wife, journeying to the dwelling of their son, in a hill settlement south of Ain Karim. Thus Mary was given to their care, and went forth with them from the edge of Jerusalem.

It was late afternoon when she entered the little village of Ain Karim and halted to inquire of certain women at the well how she might come upon the house of Zacharias, the priest.

They answered her words with courtesy, pointing the way. Yet, even as they spoke, she perceived that they gazed at her strangely, as though there was a matter they yearned to reveal, and yet could not. And while they lingered before her, uncertain and wavering, a crone who stood nearby, hearing the name of Zacharias, cried from her toothless mouth that there was a madness upon him.

"Nay, nay . . ." said one of the women quickly, for she had seen fear in the face of the girl.

They turned to her then, striving to speak kindly, and she perceived their own concern for the beloved rabbi. Nay, there was no madness upon him . . . the Lord would not have it so. Yet none could deny that a strange and perplexing thing had come about. . . .

In the autumn past, when he and Elizabeth returned from Jerusalem, where he had gone to serve in the great temple, truly he was altered in both manner and spirit. Behold, he who had been teacher and counselor to all within the village now spoke with none, and had laid the matter of his duties within the hands of a younger priest. In truth, there were those who declared that his voice had departed from him, that some demon of silence had seized him, rendering him dumb. Yet how was a demon to seize upon one who was as holy as an

31

angel of the Lord? It was a thing not to be explained, and all the village sorrowed because of it.

Having heard them, Mary thanked them in seemly words and drew her donkey from the stone trough wherein he had stilled his thirst. And she hastened from the well that she might seek her cousins, her spirit sorely troubled for their sake.

The house of Zacharias was a humble stone dwelling given beauty by the flowering creepers upon its walls, the fig tree casting shade upon its doorsill. Even as she hastened toward it, quickening the steps of the donkey, Mary perceived who it was that stood in the cooling shadows of the open doorway, taking up a water jar as though to set forth for the well.

Elizabeth was a tall and slender woman in the middle years of her life, and thus certain locks of her gleaming hair were edged with white. Her face, warmly tinted by the southern sun, had the delicate beauty of an image wrought from clay uncommonly pure by hands uncommonly skilled. She was clad in a long dark tunic falling to her shapely feet, yet not even the graceful folds loose about her body concealed that she was far advanced in the bearing of a little child.

Mary halted the donkey with a single word of command. Then, near to weeping in her joy, she sprang down and ran through the stirred dust, her arms outflung, her voice thickened by tears.

"Hail, Elizabeth. . . ."

Astonished and in wonder, Elizabeth embraced the girl, reaching out to her with yearning arms, holding her tenderly against the heart which had known undivided love for her since the day of her birth. Yet, in this moment of rejoicing, she was stricken by such a poverty of words that she was able to utter no more than a common courtesy of the tongue.

"Hail, Mary. . . ."

It was said that the Lord had bestowed upon Elizabeth a

gift akin to that of angels, for often there came to her a knowledge of things undisclosed, unproclaimed. So it was that now she drew apart from the girl and, falling upon her knees, cried out in a voice of wonder, *"Blessed are you among women!"*

At her words, there came upon Mary a sense of release as kindly as a blessing. Truly, she thought, the Lord has spoken to my sister, revealing all that I knew not how to say. For a moment, they were stilled and wordless, in a silence not unlike the hush of prayer. In the radiance cast through the open doorway by the setting of the sun, tears gleamed on Elizabeth's saintly face.

"How is it," she asked humbly, "that the mother of my Lord should come to me?"

And Mary, filled with a great gladness, answered, "My soul does magnify the Lord . . . for behold, henceforth all generations shall call me blessed. . . ."

Afterward, when they had unburdened their hearts, one to the other, Mary learned the nature of that which had befallen Zacharias.

Being one of the priests descended from Aaron, he was required to go forth to Jerusalem once during each year, that he might serve for seven days in the great temple.

This temple, magnificent and beautiful, had been rebuilt by Herod, out of his desire to surpass the earlier structure brought into being by Solomon. It was a place of marble colonnades, stately courts, fragrant and burnished cedar, walls and ceiling wrought of gold, gates fashioned of Corinthian bronze. And before the innermost shrine, where none but the High Priest might enter, there hung a veil woven in the rich and lovely colors of earth, sea, and fire.

With other priests of Aaron, Zacharias had gone forth to the performing of certain sacred rites, the kindling of incense, the sacrifice of slain animals, the tending of the holy lamps, the restoring of the shewbread. And in the casting of lots by which these duties were divided, it fell to him to burn incense as an offering to the Lord. Thus, at a sign from the priest offering the sacrificial lamb, Zacharias went on unclad feet within the innermost temple, holy with silence, where a golden altar stood before the shimmering veil. Burning coals had been borne to this altar, and upon them he cast the incense, that it might ascend before the Lord in a white and fragrant cloud.

Suddenly, he was aware of an uncommon radiance and, lifting his eyes, he beheld at the right of the altar a young man who stood quietly, with folded hands. And even as he was seized by terror, perceiving that the stranger was not of earth, a gentle voice sounded in his ears.

"Fear not, Zacharias, for your prayers are heard, and your wife, Elizabeth, shall bear a son, and you shall call his name John. And you shall have joy and gladness, and many shall rejoice at his birth. For he shall be great in the sight of the Lord . . . and shall be filled with the Holy Spirit. And many of the children of Israel shall he turn unto the Lord."

Yet, even as he listened, Zacharias was filled with doubt. Even though he had uttered a thousand prayers for the blessing of a son, even though he had abandoned no portion of his faith in their fulfillment, in this moment he stood obdurate and unbelieving, uncertain that such tidings were of the Lord.

Thus he answered in syllables utterly without trust.

"Whereby shall I know this?"

And the messenger said, "I am Gabriel who stands in the presence of God, by whom I was sent to bear you these tidings. And because you have not believed my words, you shall be stricken dumb, and shall speak no more, until they are fulfilled."

The worshipers beyond were stirring uneasily, concerned that Zacharias should have lingered for such a length of time within the shrine. Then, suddenly, he came forth, white and shaken, his face set in the dazed manner of one who has looked upon a vision. Yet he could utter no sound, not even before the disquieted Elizabeth. It was only after he had seized a stylus and tablet and written his words, that she knew what had befallen him.

With each day, after their return to the village, he had gone forth into the hills, even as now, giving hours to solitude and prayer, shamed and humbled that he had doubted the message of the Lord. Yet in three more moons, his son would be born. . . .

Until that time had come, she would abide with Elizabeth, Mary said to herself. For three unburdened months, they would dwell together, sharing the simple pattern of the days, the light laughter and tender words which rise from womanly hearts, setting their hands to the tending of the house, the kneading of the daily bread, the bearing of water from the well, the fashioning of swaddling clothes for the little John.

Long afterward she would recall the evenings of quiet companionship, with the light of the kindled lamp gleaming upon the humble room, and upon the faces of her brethren, glorified by their own serenity.

In a little time, her own child would be born. . . . A great tenderness welled up within her at the thought. Thus she put aside the fears upon her, and dwelt upon the words with which Elizabeth had counseled her.

"Wait upon the Lord, be of good courage, and He shall strengthen your heart."

V.

THE SEASON OF THE BARLEY HARVEST WAS PAST, THE RIPPLED wealth of the wheat fields had fallen beneath the sickle, the labor of gleaming and winnowing was ended. At the rising of the moon, a caravan came to Nazareth, halting in a parched and empty field beyond the walls. Almost at once, fires sprang up against the dusk, the quiet of eventide became clamorous with voices, with the lamenting of camels, the braying of an ass. Those who had journeyed throughout the heat of the day rejoiced in the thought of food and rest, laughed and spoke and called, one to the other, as they made ready to break the evening bread, to pass the night in slumber beneath the stars.

A small figure slipped from the back of a donkey, led the animal to a stone trough beside the well, and thence into the village beyond. After three moons, Mary had returned. And though her heart yearned for the things of home, the arms of her mother, the face of Joseph, her spirit was both grave and troubled, and she shrank from that which lay before her. For the hour had come, the time was upon her, when she must reveal to those she loved that which was known only to Elizabeth.

The travelers bade her farewell with little of interest. She had ridden the long miles quietly and without complaint, yet had taken no part in the words about her, lifting her voice neither in merry banter nor in desultory talk. She had tended her small donkey, kept to her own thoughts, and remained a stranger. "A maid of Nazareth," they said of her, "pleasing yet shy beyond reason, with scarcely a word to say for herself...." And before she had passed from the yellow light of the supper fires into the darkness, even before the sound of her donkey's feet had merged with the distance and silence, they had forgotten her utterly.

It was the hour of evening bread, and the streets of the village were empty of all save a small group of craftsmen and farmers returning from the market at Lydda. They trudged past her in the darkness and, with words quiet-spoken and weary, went their divided ways. She stood for a time by the well, drinking deeply of the cool, living water, hearing the wind of God in the boughs of the olive trees, savoring the ancient fragrance of dew-wet grasses and ripening vineyards. How different, she thought, is this lovely and abundant land from the desert wilderness of Judea . . . how different, and how blessed.

The streets of the village were emptied now, for each man sat within his own house, at the dearly earned bread of his own table. A pale radiance gleamed from the open doorways, where kindled lamp wicks floated in saucers of oil, and such a lamp was burning in the shop of Joseph.

Her heart quickened, crying out within her: How is it with Joseph this night? No word had come from him, nor did she know whether it was in anger or perplexity that he had looked upon her departure. In truth, he had cause for both, for it was an unwonted thing for a betrothed girl to go forth upon a journey without the consent of the beloved. Yet Joseph, being gentle of heart, rich in understanding . . .

Thus she hastened to the open door of the carpenter shop, the donkey following after her, his small feet thudding in the damp and quiet dust of the street.

It seemed a length of years since she had stood, as now, on the trodden path, in the shelter of the fig tree. She recalled how

37

it was that she had lingered here on a certain night more than three moons past, yearning to pass within, to speak with Joseph for a little time, yet forbearing, lest such a deed be thought unmaidenly.

Now, such fears seemed the trifling anxieties of an untaught girl, and she knew no concern for them. Instead, she tethered the donkey to the bough of the tree and, without reluctance, entered the doorway. Her light footfalls gave forth no sound and, for a little time, she stood in silence amid the sweet fragrance of sawn wood and shavings, gazing into the single room beyond.

The young carpenter sat at a sturdy table of his own making. He had finished with his evening meal, save for a crust of barley bread and some pottage remaining within a wooden bowl. Now he leaned near the wavering light of the lamp, studying a scroll of the holy law and searching, in the manner of a reverent man, for a means of being more just to his brothers, and thus more pleasing to the eyes of God. He was clad in a smock soiled with the labors of the day, and so thin with wear that the flesh of one shoulder had been thrust through an unmended rent in the fabric. His hair lay rumpled upon his head, falling over the fingers of one long and slender hand scarred by the striving of many years. And there was upon his face such a measure of sweet tenderness that the heart of Mary yearned toward him, unafraid.

He had not heard her enter and, lifting his eyes suddenly, beheld her upon the threshold, watching him in silence. Whereupon, he leaped to his feet, thrusting aside the table in his eagerness to come to her, but she put forth her hand, and would not have it so. They stood wordless, then, each gazing upon the other, and he saw that some subtle change had come upon her, as though she had aged in wisdom and in grace. Whereas she perceived that he had been wounded to the heart because of her . . . that his eyes, seeking her own, were troubled and bewildered. And her heart trembled within her.

Nay, she thought in despair, he does not know what has come to pass. In truth, I had hoped that it might be revealed to him, even as to me . . . that I might be spared the telling. For how is he to believe the words of my lips?

"I have only now returned," she began, slowly, "seeing not even my mother as yet. . . ."

He asked, "You did not make the journey alone?"

"Nay, it was arranged by Zachary that I should travel with a caravan bound for Capernaum. A pleasing company. . . ."

He made no answer, and she was frightened by his silence. Yet how had she thought he would greet her as before? Surely he recalled, even as he gazed upon her face, how it was that she had gone forth, neither by his leave nor with his knowledge, that she had remained in another village for a length of many days, with no word to him save a brief message borne by Cleophas. Forgive me, beloved, she pleaded silently, if I have wounded and shamed you. . . .

"Your cousin Elizabeth?" he inquired, then. "And what of the child?"

"A son with the might of Samson," and Mary smiled, thinking of the lusty voice and broad fists of this babe whose strength and size were an amazement to all of the village.

And she yearned, in that moment, to tell him all that had come about concerning the child's naming.

"He shall be called John," Elizabeth had said. "John, gift of God."

"Wherefore?" asked those about her. "Seeing that none of your brethren are called by this name. . . ."

Then Zacharias took up a wax tablet and stylus and wrote firmly, that they might know his will: *His name is John.* And as he strove to make the matter plain before them, lest they have no understanding, the bonds of his silence were sundered, and speech returned to him. To those of the village this was indeed a great marvel, and the story was revealed to every passing traveler, as Mary would have revealed it now. Yet, since Joseph had no heart for wonders, she spoke otherwise, saying simply, "They have given him the name of John."

Again the charged silence rose between them. Then Joseph made a step toward her, holding forth his hands in a manner both supplicating and humble.

"What has come to you, my darling?" he asked, in sorrow. "You have returned to me a stranger. . . ."

And now, seeing that the moment was indeed upon her, Mary was stricken with blinding terror. Yet she concealed this from his eyes and spoke without wavering.

"Joseph," she said, quietly, "I am to bear a child."

Despite their gentleness, her words assailed him with the strength of a lash, so that he fell back from her as from an unsparing blow. Even while he stared at her, the sweat of mortal anguish gleamed upon him, the color went from his face, rendering it as cold and grey as stone. Yet she stood before him resolute and unfaltering, the radiance of the kindled lamp shining in her eyes. Slowly, numbly, he lifted one hand and passed it across his brow in the manner of one who seeks to rid himself of a dream of horror.

"A child. . . ." The words were dazed and unbelieving.

Behold, the girl thought, I have wounded him utterly, I have shattered the heart within his bosom. And, in wrenching pity, she reached forth her hand to him.

"Joseph . . ."

Whereupon he turned from her, nor would he look upon her face again. His arms hung lifeless at his sides, his head was bowed beneath the weight of his wretchedness.

"Whose child?" he asked hoarsely.

"It is the child of God."

There was a little space of silence. Then his head was lifted, his voice startled and strange.

"What is it you have said?"

She answered again, "It is the child of God."

And now he turned to her in wonder, repeating the words she had uttered.

"Of God?"

"By His will, I have been chosen to bear the child of promise, the deliverer."

He came forward slowly, setting his hands upon her small shoulders, speaking in tones of great gentleness.

"Mary, Mary . . . you have made a long and burdensome journey. Truly, you are shattered with weariness. . . ."

"Nay, Joseph," she said, quietly, "you need have no fear that a madness has seized me. I have spoken truth, and I . . . I beseech you not to doubt the words of my mouth. Behold, we are betrothed, and there is love between us. . . ." She paused, and when she spoke again, her voice was so low, it was scarcely to be heard. "Surely you cannot believe I have sinned against you. . . ."

He twisted his hands like a man cruelly bound, seeking to break free. His breath quickened, and sweat stood thick upon his brow.

"I . . . I cannot say," he burst forth, at last.

She perceived that his spirit was retreating from her, and stood, heart-stricken, before him. The promise of a child of God had filled her with joy. Belief that this would be made known to Joseph also, had given her rest, even as the counsel of Elizabeth had brought her peace. Yet now the warm fabric of her dreaming was torn from her, leaving her unclad before the world, a terrified girl dishonored and in despair.

"If . . ." began Joseph, slowly. He turned to her again, a wretched hope rising to his eyes. "If it has come to you to

41

regret our betrothal, then truly there are other ways . . . other words you might have spoken.

She answered, unwavering, "I have uttered the truth."

And now she sought to share with him some portion of the wonder and the glory, saying how it was that she had beheld before her one with lifted head and folded hands, with a radiance of holiness about him. She would have a child, he had told her, for she was chosen of God.

". . . *you shall bring forth a son and call his name Jesus . . . and he shall reign over the House of Jacob forever, and of his kingdom, there shall be no end. . . .*"

"The promised deliverer," said Joseph, slowly. "Indeed, there is no generation of Israel which has not told this tale a thousand times. It may be that you have thought of it, dreamed of it, until you are possessed by it. . . ."

She perceived with what desperation he sought to deliver her from shame, yet she said again, "Nay, Joseph, I have spoken truth."

For a moment, he stared at her, rendered wordless by her answer.

"Oh, Mary!" he gasped out at last. It was a sound of immeasurable anguish. Then swiftly, brokenly, he said, "May God walk beside you. . . ." And turning from her, he stumbled forth into the street.

Surely hours passed while she stood alone within the humble room, while the flame wavered, and the lonely sound of crickets rose sorrowfully from a clump of grasses beyond the door. Nay, she said to herself, it cannot be true that he, Joseph, has turned his face from me. Nay, she thought dully, it is not to be. We are betrothed, and there is love between us. . . . She stared unseeingly at the table before her, at the remnants of the evening meal, the abandoned scroll, heart-stricken and unmoving.

He has turned from me utterly, she thought, as will all others

42

of the village, even our kinsmen. And though it was known to her that Anne would never abandon her, she found little consolation in the thought, knowing that her shame would break her mother's heart.

Yes, truly, Joseph would put her away, no longer desiring to take her as his wife. And when at length this had come about, and his reason made known to the elders, they would condemn her to stoning and name her an adultress before the world.

On a certain day in her childhood, she had witnessed such a thing in the streets of Nazareth . . . the clamor and the mob, the shouts of derision, the cries of hate, the taking up and casting of stones by men and women suddenly become virtuous in their own eyes, vengeful in the name of the Lord. She remembered the accused girl, young and lovely to look upon, too heavy with her unborn babe to flee from those who pursued her . . . how at length, she had fallen in the dust of the street and lain, quivering, in her own blood. And the image brought a great shuddering upon her, yet her fear was not for death, but for the dishonoring of those she loved. And such a measure of desolation came to her that she covered her face with her shaken hands and wept.

Afterward, when her sorrow had spent itself somewhat, she made her way out of the shop and along the streets spread with patches of moonlight and the shadows of leaves. The village was silent and some of the doors were darkened. Already many had offered their prayers and quenched their lamps and lain down to slumber upon their bed mats.

At the sight of her own house, her heart quickened, and she hastened her steps, meaning to cast herself within the tender arms of Anne and reveal the burden of shame and sorrow upon her. But Mary Cleophas was there, and so the moment passed unfulfilled. Yet for a little time, her wretchedness was forgotten in the joyous greetings of her mother and sister, their pleasure in her return. After the way of women, they were filled to bursting with word of their months apart, with eagerness to speak of Zacharias and Elizabeth and the newborn child, with tidings of village joys and sorrows which had come to pass in Mary's absence. It was very late and she was wearied beyond the telling when, at last, she lay down upon her own bed mat beneath the familiar window open to the stars.

Yet slumber would not come to her, but images of torment only . . . the stricken face of Joseph, the loving trust in the eyes of Anne, the outraged elders rending their garments. Who among them would believe that she spoke truth, that she had indeed beheld a mist of light within her own house, and one who stood with lifted head and folded hands, saying, "Do not be afraid, Mary, for you have found grace with God. . . ." Throughout their lives, the elders had spoken of the messengers of the Lord, had told many wonders concerning them. And yet . . . and *yet,* such things were matters of power and glory, and did not come about in one's own village. Nay, they would declare, the girl lies to conceal her own dishonor, she has spoken blasphemy and is deserving of death. . . .

Thus, troubled and unsleeping, she rose with the first glimmering light of day and went forth from the house into the garden. The redness of dawn had stained the sky, wind stirred the cloudy branches of the olive tree, in the distance a cock was crowing. A beautiful day was beginning, but the heart of the girl was so heavy with sorrow that she had no thought for the morning.

After a time she reached forth and plucked a soft blue flower opening in the dew since, growing apart from all others, it appeared to know a loneliness not unlike her own. And, as she knelt there, her face half hidden by the gleaming darkness of her hair, she heard a footfall upon the path, and a voice spoke beside her.

"Mary . . ."

44

Whereupon she lifted her eyes and beheld the face of Joseph filled with contrition and shame. Like a penitent lad, he flung himself down before her and bowed his head.

"Last night," he said humbly, "it was in my mind to shatter the bond of our espousal. I would refuse to take you in marriage, not believing that you spoke the truth. Yet when I had done with weeping and fallen into slumber, a dream came upon me, in which I beheld one like a young priest. . . ."

Mary's heart quickened. The radiance of the morning shone forth in her eyes.

"Yes, Joseph," she said, gently.

"And it seemed that he spoke to me, saying I should set aside my doubts, for the child you will bear is indeed the promised deliverer.

"Yet at first, I had no faith in the dream. I said to myself that it had come to me only out of my love and longing for you, my yearning to believe in you utterly. I thought: What manner of man am I, that I would take to wife one who bears the child of another? I said to myself: Wonders do not come to a humble village, to a laborer and a maid. Would God choose such a one as I to bring His son to manhood? I said: In truth, there will be born of our people a deliverer, even as the prophets have declared. These things are written. They will come to pass in God's own time. Yet not to me, nor to my betrothed. . . ."

"The same thoughts came to me," said Mary, quietly.

Joseph lifted his head.

"Then I said to myself: Who am I, to say what is to be, or not to be? For I am but a man, and it is not for me to judge the holy will of God . . . but only to perform it. Thus, I asked His forgiveness for my doubts and now, my beloved, I ask yours. . . ."

His voice faltered and was brought to silence, broken by

shame and misery. An ineffable tenderness came upon the face of the girl, and she reached forth one hand and placed it gently upon his disordered hair.

"Oh, Joseph, I do forgive you!"

Whereupon he took her hands in both his own, and they knelt together in the ripening light. Again the song of thanksgiving rose from the temple of Mary's heart, so that she whispered wordlessly and in wonder, "My soul does magnify the Lord."

VI.

ALL MANNER OF TRAVELERS THRONGED THE STONY ROAD WHICH led up the long limestone hill to Bethlehem, a small village on the edge of the Judean wilderness. They had been three days upon the way and now, with the going down of the sun and the rising of a cold winter wind, some of the desolation of the wilderness itself fell upon Mary's heart.

It was known to her that, within a little time, she must bring forth her child. Alone with her husband in the midst of strangers, she was frightened by that which lay before her, stricken with a yearning for her mother which was not to be fulfilled.

Had Anne lived but another moon, she would have looked upon her grandson, held him to her breast, laid him for the first time in the arms of his young mother. Tears rose to Mary's eyes at the thought and she turned her head quickly, lest Joseph behold her sorrow, for already his heart was heavy because of her.

He had set forth from Nazareth filled with bitter anger that a young wife awaiting her first-born child must travel long miles on the back of a donkey for the reason that the Roman emperor suddenly desired all Jews to be counted, and a census made. Every Jew was commanded to return, with neither question nor dissent, to the city of his own family, and there

47

were sent forth threats of unsparing punishment for any who did not obey.

Thus Joseph and Mary, being of the House of David, had turned their faces to Bethlehem, looking with dread, as did many others, to all that was required of them. The season of winter was miserably cold and windy on the heights. The roads were rough and crowded, the journey so costly as to be, for many, a bitter hardship. Yet none were spared, neither the ill nor the ailing, the aged nor the blind, nor girls who, like Mary, knew that before the journey was ended, their children would be born.

In the beginning, she had regarded the journey with serenity.

"Except that we go up to Bethlehem," she said, quietly, "how are the words of Micah to be fulfilled?"

For it was of Bethlehem that the prophet had spoken, calling the village by its ancient name: *And you, Ephrath, though you are small among the thousands of Judah, yet from you shall come he that is to be the ruler in Israel, whose origin is from old, from everlasting.*

Ephrath . . . Bethlehem. This night they would enter the walls of the little town and there, also on this night, her child might be born, yet who could say where or in what manner, or whether there would be any to solace her in this hour of a woman's deepest loneliness. The Nazareth midwife, being of another tribe, had journeyed to yet another village, yet before her departure, she had spoken words of consolation, so that now Mary clung to them as to gentle and kindly hands.

"There is no cause for fear, my daughter, seeing that all will be well with you. A little time of anguish, truly, but even that is soon past. So it shall be. To Rachel these things are quickly revealed."

Yet the very name of Rachel brought fear upon the girl, inasmuch as she recalled another Rachel, her own ancestor, who had closed her eyes in death beside this very road, and was buried here, after the birth of her son. They passed her tomb, both remembering what had come to pass, yet saying no word of the matter.

At the hour of midday, Mary had been stricken with small thrusts of pain which grew deeper and more agonizing with the passing of the hours. Now she set her teeth against them lest they cause her to cry out. Her slender hands were crossed upon the bosom of her long blue cloak, and her head was bowed in prayer. Joseph, beside her, trudged uncomplainingly, easing his weariness with the aid of a staff borne in his hand, yet she knew him to be spent beyond the telling. Even the donkey, she saw with pity, drooped forlornly as he plodded up the hill.

Bethlehem stood high on a length of bountiful countryside rich, in the months of summer, with vineyards and olive groves and fig trees rising in terraces of greenery, one above the other, a village of houses squared and white, climbing upward against the green of the hills. Yet now winter was upon the land and the hills were barren and brown, the vineyards stripped and naked.

To Mary and Joseph, as to all others of their people, Bethlehem was a name which recalled centuries of Jewish history. Thus they gazed with tenderness upon the bleak hillsides, for it was here that David had kept watch over the flocks of his father in the years of his boyhood. To this same Bethlehem had come Ruth, the gentle Moabite girl, the beloved alien, that she might care for her aged mother-in-law, Naomi. And it was here also that Boaz had beheld Ruth gleaning in his own fields and, gazing upon her with eyes of love, had made her his wife.

Now the pale rays of the wintry sun faded from sight behind a length of cloud, and a cold wind swept upon those who traveled. At once there was a stirring among them, a sudden

49

anxiety which caused them to strive forward quickly and with rivalry, jostling and crowding ahead, fearful lest night overtake them before they could reach and enter the gate.

A thin film of snow had covered the hills beyond, where hundreds of sheep were huddled together in the manner of a vast and roughly woven blanket, bleating plaintively. Throughout the day, the shepherds had led them in and out of the hollows that they might seek wintry grass with which to stay their hunger.

The number of shepherds in the region of Bethlehem was not to be counted. Indeed, no sight was more familiar than the sight of these men, each in his rough garment, with a staff to bring him up and down, a crook with which he might draw to safety a sheep or a lamb in danger. Some of the shepherds had grown old in the leading of their flocks, others were lads beginning to learn the way, red-cheeked and merry, heedless of the bitter cold. Many bore bundles of brushwood upon their backs for, with the coming of night, they would huddle together around a small crackling fire, keeping watch over their flocks. Each tended his sheep with utter devotion, saved them from danger, healed the injured among them, lifted to his shoulder the ailing and helpless. Nor was it an uncommon thing for a shepherd to lay down his life for his flock, seeing that lions and leopards came forth from the chalk-hill caves at nightfall, seeking to prey upon the tender lambs.

With the going down of the sun, the sight of hills and flocks dimmed and merged with the darkness. Lights sprang up, the lights of small villages beyond the road, the wavering flames of supper fires where certain travelers had halted for the night, the slow-moving radiance of hundreds of lanterns with which others plodded on.

Now, suddenly, Mary could no longer conceal the anguish upon her, and a stricken gasp rose, unbidden, to her lips. At once, Joseph turned to her, startled and afraid.

"Beloved, are you in pain?"

She nodded and beheld panic rising in his eyes. With trembling fingers he drew the woolen cloak about her, so that it sheltered her more closely, as though by force of love alone he could strengthen the fabric against the bitter wind.

"If we can but enter before the gate is closed," he said, then. "Surely, once we are within the village . . ."

His words were a prayer, beseeching shelter for her in this troubled hour, shelter and comfort and warmth. She perceived the fear in his face and reached forth and touched him gently, seeking to comfort him as they waited outside the gate, with the throng about them.

Within, a guard paced before a large room in which sat a publican. To him must be paid a tax on every man and animal, on the goods of all travelers, before they might pass beyond the wall. It was no matter of surprise that the publicans were despised throughout the land, for they were Jews who served the hated Romans, without concern for their own people. Indeed, it was known to all that they enriched their purses by demanding taxes beyond those set by the Roman governor, yet should any traveler protest, he might be named a smuggler and thus flogged or cast into prison.

No matter who stood first at the gate, the rich were given leave to enter while the poor, such as Mary and Joseph, must wait unsheltered in the night. Caravans, one after the other, were summoned before them, bearing the goods of many lands, oil and wine, dates, perfumes and spices, silken fabrics, jewels and gold. And then, even as their time was at hand, Joseph was struck aside by a slave who pushed his way through the multitude with sticks and shouts.

"Make way, make way!" he cried with arrogance. "Make way for a noble son of the House of David!"

Six Nubian slaves, in matched livery, came forth bearing a litter in which reclined a Jew from the city of Jerusalem who

51

had come about his wealth by turning his face from his own people and receiving, instead, the Roman conquerors. In truth, he wore not only the Roman cloak, but the Roman insolence.

"Make way! Make way!" cried the slave again. And the publican, beholding a man of riches at the gate, admitted him quickly, with servile deference.

Because such injustice was not an uncommon thing to either Mary or Joseph, they bore it with patience and resignation. At length, just before the gate was closed for the night, they were summoned within and commanded to pay their tax. It was a matter which required little time, since they possessed but a single animal and bore no goods beyond a small store of food and some clothing. The publican seized their money and motioned them forward, impatiently and with contempt.

"The inn is but a little distance ahead," said Joseph, then, but Mary made no answer, knowing that his hope was vain, not to be fulfilled. From her place above the throng about her, she perceived the number of travelers clamoring, in weariness and anxiety, at the gates of the inn . . . the young, the aged, the feeble, the strong, even girls like herself, heavy with children soon to be born.

There was but a single inn in the village, a great walled court with an upper story divided into two great rooms, one being for women and the other for men, both crowded to the very stones. In the center of the court was a sleeping platform near the warmth of a fire and, around the walls, roofed spaces where animals might be tethered and costly goods sheltered from rain or snow. Yet on this night so vast was the throng of travelers that many slept upon the unsheltered earth of the open court, wrapping themselves in their cloaks, lying close to the warmth of their beasts.

"In truth," said Joseph, as they halted before the gates of

the inn, "so great a throng is not to be received. Yet if I go forth and plead with the innkeeper ... surely, understanding your need..."

She sought to smile at him, but the smile was of her lips only. Her eyes were stricken with sudden terror as pain, swift and sharp as a sickle, cut through and across her. And, in that moment, her heart cried out for her mother, for Mary Cleophas, Elizabeth, Rachel ... any woman who would turn to her, comfort her, save her from her own fear. She and Joseph had asked none to share their journey, knowing that, for her sake and the sake of the child, they must travel very slowly, halting often to give her rest. They had thought to seek friends and kinsmen in Bethlehem, yet now it was plain before them that only by the strangest chance would one behold a familiar face in this multitude of travelers.

The crowd increased and strengthened, straining toward the gates of the inn. Mary tried to say to herself, seeing that there was a measure of comfort in the thought, "In truth, they are as weary as I, as lonely and as wretched. ..." For she heard the children weeping against the soft, gentle voices of their mothers.

"Just a little longer, my darling. Once we are inside the inn . . ."

Once we are inside the inn. . . . It was a hope, a prayer, a promise on the lips of all. Oh, what was keeping Joseph for so great a length of time? Suddenly, it seemed a length of hours since he strode away, seeking shelter for her. Could it be that, in the crowded and clamorous darkness, he was unable to make his way back to her? Panic smote her, so that another pain wrenched her body, a pain deeper and sharper than before. Straightening with difficulty when it had gone from her, she sought to peer through the dimness, yet Joseph was not to be seen.

A slave pushed past her, running, shoving aside the children

53

who wept for hunger, bearing a platter of smoking meat and bread for the man he called master.

Suddenly, the girl perceived her husband making his way toward her through the throng, his face white and set, his eyes filled with terror. And so, after the way of women, she concealed the anguish upon her and awaited him with a smile.

"Forgive me that I was so long away," he said heavily.

"Please, beloved," she answered, "do not concern yourself."

"It . . . it is no easy thing I must tell you," he began, miserably.

Whereupon she put her hand within his own and, leaning down, gazed upon his troubled face.

"What is it you would say?"

His eyes were filled with unshed tears.

"There is no room at the inn."

She could not speak, for again the pain assailed her, so that her lips were white with agony. Yet she held herself rigid and unyielding, that he should not know the time was upon her, upon them both.

"I spoke to the innkeeper, saying how it is with us," Joseph went on. "Already he is harried unto death with the needs of the travelers, but his wife, having borne children of her own, was moved to pity, and said that we should have, at least, the warmth and shelter of the stable." Some of the tears fell upon his face, and his voice broke as he added bitterly, "*A stable!*"

Yet Mary's heart rejoiced in the thought that any roof, however humble, would shelter them from the night.

"Should we, of the House of David, look with scorn upon a stable?" she asked, gently. "In truth, David often slept in a stable with his flock . . . it may be that even *this* stable was known to him. And yet he was a king. . . ."

Comforted by her words, he smiled into her clear eyes and held her hand, for a moment, against his face. Then, taking up the lead-strap of the donkey, he made his way through the multitude and through the gate.

In the hills of Bethlehem, caves had long served as stables and were warm and sweet with hay. This one possessed rough stone walls and a roof of wide beams laid with thatch. Beside a manger some oxen placidly chewed their cuds, unmoved by the coming of strangers. A few lambs, being weak and new-born, lay close to the warmth of their mothers.

Joseph lifted the girl from the donkey, unloaded their meager goods. The warmest cloak he spread across the hay, that Mary might rest upon it. He fed the donkey in haste, gave it water, and went to sit beside his young wife, shaken by fear and pity for her utter anguish. She held tightly to his hands, gripping them for comfort and strength as the pains assailed her.

Isolated by their ordeal, they were scarcely aware of the voices which rose in the courtyard of the inn, some raucous and drunken, some lifted in anger, some loud with laughter, vile with curses. Mingled among them were the groans of camels, the braying of donkeys, the barking of dogs. A length of time passed and, one after another, the sounds ceased. At last, stillness came upon the inn, broken only by the distant cries of jackals and hyenas out in the night where shepherds watched their flocks in the glow of small brushwood fires.

And the silent hills of all the earth looked to the sky and waited for a Star.

VII.

IN THE CLAY-SAUCER LAMP, A WICK FLOATED IN OIL, ITS FLAME casting a soft, uneven radiance upon the stable and the family sheltered within its rough stone walls, near to the oxen, the ewes, and the lambs.

The oxen stood like huge black shadows in the dimness, chewing their cuds in unceasing reflection beside the low manger in which Mary had laid her newborn son, that they might warm him. Many times in her childhood, she herself had been warmed by the clover-laden breath of field animals when she and her parents slept beneath the stars on their way to the Passover at Jerusalem.

Wrapped in the blue woolen cloak, she lay at peace upon the fragrant hay. Joseph gazed at the small, pale face and it seemed to him that her very youthfulness was pathetic to look upon. Yet now both pain and fear had departed from her, and her eyes were filled with dreams as she beheld the sleeping child.

"In truth, he is different from all others," she said, softly.

Drawing near to her, her husband took her hand within his own and together they gazed upon the beautiful and perfect babe. Yet in Joseph's eyes, he seemed little more wondrous than every child. For to Joseph, even the smallest newborn lambs, brought forth from their mothers by the pangs of birth, seemed miraculous and awesome as bearers of life.

He had helped to cleanse the tender flesh of the babe with oil from a cruse in their baskets and, together, they had wound him in swaddling clothes, wide lengths of soft linen passed about his little body from his chest to his feet. Then, borne in his mother's arms, and in the folds of a woolen cloak, he had been placed in the straw-filled manger where, almost at once, he fell into untroubled slumber.

Past weariness in her joy, Mary lay quietly, her dark eyes radiant with pride and tenderness as she beheld the sweet countenance of her little son. And now, being released from anxiety and fear, Joseph recalled that he had not broken the evening bread and was assailed by hunger. He brought forth from their baskets portions of fruit and cheese to be shared with his wife and, together, they ate and knew rest and spoke in wonder of the child, and were content.

A little time later, Mary slumbered and her husband, watching lest some harm come to her, folded his own cloak about her and sat in silence. Surely hours passed as he kept the tender vigil, roused by the lightest stir from mother or child, or from the animals whose deep breaths filled the stable with warmth and a sense of humble companionship, in the still watches of the night.

So deep and gentle a silence lay about them that even Joseph was near to slumber when there came a sound of voices beyond the walls, lifted as though they dealt with some matter of haste and wonder, the tread of feet, and then a light knocking upon the rough wood of the door.

Even as Joseph roused in astonishment, Mary rose up, wakened by the clamor, concerned for her child, reaching forth her hand to Joseph, that he might stay her fears.

"How is it that any would knock at such an hour, desiring to enter a stable?"

"Have no fear, beloved. It may be that another traveler seeks shelter in desperate need. . . ."

57

"Yes, truly, it must be so. Then hasten and open to them, for the night is cold. . . ."

They whispered quickly, quietly, together as the sound of knocking came again. Then Joseph opened the door and beheld before him a gathering of humble shepherds, roughly clad men wet with wind-swept snow. One, a man of many years, bent beneath the weight of age, had thick white eyebrows and a grizzled white beard. Others were younger, one being no more than a lad, his cheeks reddened by the cold, his eyes big with wonder. And, indeed, there was not one among them who did not appear moved by some breathless awe.

The aged man stared at Joseph with faded eyes.

"Is there, within this stable, a newborn babe lying in a manger?"

Whereupon Joseph nodded and would have spoken, had not a swift radiance filled the old shepherd's face, a joyous cry burst forth from his lips.

"The sign!"

In haste, yet without disorder, they crowded into the stable and fell down upon their knees beside the manger and knelt for a time without speaking, their faces filled with worship. Tears gleamed upon the weathered cheeks of the old one, and he began the telling of a strange story.

"We were out upon the hills beside our fire, keeping watch over our flocks by night, when lo, the glory of the Lord shone round us, and we were sore afraid. . . ."

Falling to their knees, they had lifted their eyes and beheld, in the sky above them, a great star which burned with an unearthly radiance against the dark silence of the night. And as they cowered upon the frozen earth, knowing terror in the sight, an angel of the Lord came upon them, and said to them, "Fear not. For behold, I bring word of great joy for you, and for all people. For there is born today, in the city of David, the promised Savior. And this shall be a sign unto you. You

58

shall find the babe wrapped in swaddling clothes and lying in a manger."

Then a chorus of joyous song poured forth from the heavens with the light of the star, and the ears of the shepherds were filled with the sound of heavenly voices lifted up to God in everlasting praise. *"Glory to God in the highest, and on earth peace, good will to men."*

Then, as swiftly as it had come, the glory departed from them. Yet the star still shone with a beckoning light, and thus the shepherds resolved to go forth, even to Bethlehem, and look upon that which the Lord had made known to them.

And when at last they turned from the stable, the first glimmer of morning was in the sky.

"Long have our people awaited this dawn," the old shepherd said, and his face was filled with glory. "Let us go forth and make known abroad that which we have seen and heard."

Joseph closed the door upon their departure, wearied by the disquieted night, and, after a little time, fell into a slumber. Then Mary lifted up the babe from the manger, and cradled him against her breast, and laid her young face against the sweetness of his cheek.

And she recalled how it was that word of him had come to her on an evening hushed with the silence of prayer. *"Do not be afraid, Mary, for you have found favor with God."* She would bring forth a son, and she would call his name Jesus. She held the child closer and whispered the name. He would reign over the House of Jacob forever, and of his kingdom there would be no end. The Messiah, the Christ, the child anointed by the Lord . . . *hers.* Yet the thought was one of humble thanksgiving only, that she had been found worthy of so glorious a trust.

Then other words spoken by the prophets came to her, assailing her as cruelly as a blow.

". . . despised and rejected of men . . . a man of sorrows,

acquainted with grief . . . oppressed and afflicted . . . and led as a lamb to slaughter. . . ."

"*Nay!*" the cry, wrenched from her lips, was a sound more anguished than any birth pang. She held the babe tight against her breast, her heart beating with such fear that it seemed the sound of it would waken and frighten him. Then the moment passed, the terror departed from her and did not come to her again. It was as though the merciful hand of God had given her peace, and she said no more of these things, not even in her thoughts, but kept them hidden in her heart.

A little time after the making of the census, when the village ceased to be thronged with travelers, Joseph found lodgings for his family in Bethlehem. Here they would dwell, while he labored in the shop of a carpenter and Mary tended the humble little house, awaiting the day when the child might be presented in the temple at Jerusalem.

According to the ways of Israel, the first fruits of every harvest, likewise the fruits of every season, must be borne to the temple as tithes of the Lord. In the same manner, the first son born to any man must be consecrated to God, presented at the temple to receive the rites of circumcision, and the blessing of the priest. And Mary also would go up to Jerusalem, not only for the sake of her little one, but that she might be purified.

The words of the ancient law declared every mother unclean for a length of forty days after bringing forth a child, and she could be restored at the end of this time only by the laying of a gift before the Lord. Many offered a yearling lamb with neither spot nor blemish, sacrificed upon an altar of unhewn stones. Yet the poor and the humble, such as Joseph and Mary, could offer no greater gift than a pair of doves.

Thus, at the appointed time, on the fortieth day after the birth of Jesus, on a radiant morning when the wind was sweet in the trees, Joseph lifted his young wife upon the donkey and laid the child in her arms. And, journeying forth together, they went up the five steep miles to the holy city.

The great temple, with which Herod had sought to win the favor of the Jewish people, was a magnificent structure of white walls and golden towers, of marble courts and colonnades, beautiful stairs, gates wrought of gleaming bronze. Above it rose the dark and imperious walls of the Roman fortress, and from these the soldiers of the Roman emperor gazed down upon the ways of Jewish worship with utter contempt.

The temple market offered sheep and oxen, jars of oil, spices and frankincense, all things needed for the rites of sacrifice. Joseph halted before the tables of the money-changers, that the coins he had saved against this day might be changed for Jewish shekels. Roman money, used in trade by command of their conquerors, was unclean in the eyes of the priests, and so great a sum was charged for changing it to temple coin that Joseph was filled with unavailing anger. Yet, seeing that there was no help for it, he went forth, wordless, with Mary and the child, leaving the tables of the money-changers behind.

With Joseph bearing in his hand the little cage of doves, they made their way up the broad steps to the Court of Women where, according to the custom, Mary would await him. Suddenly, there was a cry, and an aged man, trembling with years and wonder, tottered to meet them. Afterward, it was said that he was Simeon, a prophet, a man of great wisdom and holiness who had lived on, past many others of his time, declaring God had promised him in a vision that he would not taste of death until he had beheld the face of the promised Savior.

Now, his faded eyes burned with a holy radiance and tears ran down the deep furrows of his weathered face as he stretched forth his arms to the child. Whereupon Mary, not knowing how it was that she was moved to such a deed, placed her son upon his bosom. For a time, he stood wordless and unmoving, gazing upon the little one. Then, lifting his eyes and voice to God, he cried out, "Lord, let Thy servant now depart in peace . . . for my eyes have seen the salvation which Thou hast prepared for all people. . . ."

There were others who, hearing his voice, drew near to the little group, made curious and wondering. And they perceived that the light of prophecy shone in Simeon's face, the spirit of prophecy spoke from his lips as he blessed the parents and the babe, declaring, "Behold, this child shall mean the fall and the rising up of many!"

There was a little space of silence. Then, turning to Mary, he pointed a bony finger at her breast.

"And thine own soul a sword shall pierce!"

At his words, a chill seized upon her frail body. She reached for her son and held him closely, almost fiercely, to her breast, setting her teeth against the terror which rose to her throat.

The aged man stumbled from them and Joseph, perceiving what disquiet was upon his wife, put his arm about her and spoke to her with gentle, reasoning words. After a little time, they moved on together, passing other couples who had brought their child to be blessed, men and women who had come to pray, to lay their tithes and sacrifices before the Lord. Priests came and went also, in richly crafted sandals and white, unblemished robes. And at times they glimpsed such women as toiled in the temple workshops.

It was known to them that more than twenty thousand priests served in the temple, each clad in pure white vestments which, being soiled, were not washed but burned, and new ones brought forth. Thus a vast number of women were required for the weaving and fashioning of both vestments and draperies. Often widows who possessed no kinsmen gave the balance of their lives to the temple workshops, dwelling within the sacred walls, living by labor and fasting and prayer. Many were withered with age, vastly wrinkled of face, toothless altogether, broken of voice, feeble of gait, yet holy beyond all others.

Such a one was Hannah, the prophetess, known to all who came within the temple gates. She had lived past the hundredth year of her life, as thin and stiff and withered as any mummy out of Egypt, her hands having the look of broken claws, her long hair hanging, sparse and ragged, about her face. The many years of her widowhood had been filled with toil, with fasting and with prayer, so that, in the extremity of her age, she appeared nearer dead than living.

Now, as Mary and Joseph approached the Court of Women, there was a shuffling sound and the aged crone, her eyes glittering with prophecy, came before the child and cried out in a thin, shrill voice, "O Lord, receive the gratitude of Thy servant, Hannah, for I have seen the child of promise, the Savior of the world!"

And she cast herself down and lay prostrate upon the floor in the manner of one humbled by the presence of holiness. Joseph, seeing that Mary was both distressed and frightened, spoke to her gently and led her forth. A little gathering of the curious halted to stare upon the prophetess and then, losing interest, passed on and left her alone.

VIII.

After the way of every village, bethlehem was filled with rumors passed from doorsill to doorsill, borne up and down the narrow streets, in and out of the shop wherein Joseph labored. Afterward, he spoke of them to Mary as they broke the evening bread together, sitting in the gleam of a single lamp, the little one asleep in his wooden cradle beside them.

Herod, it was told, had been seized by a sickness no less to be dreaded than leprosy, and was near to death. His body had grown swollen and was rotted within, so that when he sought to eat or drink, he was stricken by insupportable pain. Yet even in the worst of his sufferings, he abandoned none of his cruelty. Indeed, the disease had strengthened his barbarity, rendering him crazed and utterly without reason.

By those who served the palace, many tales of his madness were made known. In the watches of the night, they whispered, he rose up, driven by shrieking terror, believing he looked upon all he had slain, declaring their faces floated before him, pale and bodiless, dissolving in mist and shadow. Throughout the night, the ominous cries of ravens, birds of ill portent, echoed in his ears. Terror lest some enemy seek his destruction in the hours of his weakness filled him with savage and unsparing violence. Thus it was a perilous time for men to murmur that a child-king would rule in his stead, indeed had already been born to this destiny in the village of Bethlehem.

The gentle face of Joseph was grave with concern.

"A thousand times have the words been uttered . . . in the streets and in the markets, at the city gates and beside the wells. . . ."

The shepherds from whose lips they first had fallen were seized and borne like wretches before the angered king. Yet even in their terror, they were firm and unyielding in their telling of the tale, saying how it was that they had been watching their flocks by night when a streaming radiance came upon them, a voice out of the heavens spoke before them, and a great star shone forth above the stable wherein they beheld the promised child.

But the soldiers of Herod, being commanded to a stable now emptied even of lambs, found only a frightened innkeeper who told a vague and disordered story of a man and woman from another village who had halted there while the woman gave birth to a son, and then had gone their way.

"It is not known to them," said Joseph, "that we came from Nazareth."

Mary gazed at him with troubled eyes.

"Are there any who say we now dwell in Bethlehem?"

Joseph shook his head. It was said only that the king had been enraged utterly, learning none had inquired from whence the young man and woman came, or to what city they went in their departure.

"It is believed by many that we dwell in Jerusalem. For those who lingered in the temple on that day . . . who saw old Simeon bless us . . . have revealed his words concerning your little son, and the words of the prophetess also. Last night, Simeon died . . . he who declared death would not seek him out before he had beheld the Messiah. Thus the rumors have strengthened. It is being told that the child of promise has been born, that into his hands will be given the scepter of Herod."

Mary rose quickly, her eyes great with fear, and would have seized the child as though to flee with him.

"Let us go forth to Nazareth, even now, this very night, lest the soldiers of Herod come upon us. . . ."

He stayed her gently, taking her hands into his own, striving to comfort her with reasoning words.

"Would this not be a matter of suspicion in their eyes? Surely they seek a man and woman and child who appear even as we . . . a humble family from some village of the countryside. And were we halted, brought before the shepherds . . . yes, truly, our faces would be remembered in their eyes. . . ."

She stared at him, frightened and troubled, yet after a little time she was able to perceive the wisdom of his words. Only by living quietly, in the manner of any blameless couple with a young child, would they attain obscurity.

Yet no hour passed wherein she did not know the cold and nauseous taste of terror. The sound of a horseman in the street smote her heart with dread, a knocking on the doorposts of the small and humble house drove her to her feet, unsteadied and trembling. More than once, in the dark hours of the night, she lay waiting, with suspended breath, while the unbroken tread of heavy feet approached and passed the doorway.

A little time later, when Joseph returned at the going down of the sun, she perceived in his face a fear akin to her own, and went to him quickly.

"A new danger has arisen. . . ."

"Leastwise a new rumor," he answered, dryly. "A rumor out of Jerusalem, saying that while women drew water at a certain well, a princely caravan approached bearing three richly clad strangers who asked: Where is he that is born king of the Jews? . . . for we have seen his star in the east, and have come to worship him."

Even though he suffered great anguish of body and a vast uneasiness of spirit, Herod had received them with a courtesy born of unfailing guile, Joseph said. And he laid the matter before his priests and scribes and astrologers, that they might reveal in what village the promised one, the Christ, would be found. Then these spoke the name of Bethlehem, for it was written by the prophets of old: *And thou, Bethlehem, though thou art little among the thousands of Judah, out of thee shall he come forth, he who is to be ruler in Israel, whose origin is from old, from everlasting. . . .*

Whereupon the king turned to the strangers and spoke to them in artful and contriving words.

"Go forth and seek the young child, and when you have found him, bear word to me, that I may worship before him also."

And now Mary was stricken with utter terror, so that she besought her husband desperately.

"Let us flee in this very hour, not to Nazareth . . . seeing that it is ruled by Herod also . . . but to Egypt, where he may not pursue us, where our little lad may dwell in peace!"

Yet Joseph would not have it so.

"Nay, beloved, for we must await the will of the Lord."

That night they prayed long and earnestly together, in the syllables of consolation which had directed the uncertain steps of their fathers before them.

"The Lord is my light and my salvation; whom shall I fear?

"The Lord is the strength of my life; of whom shall I be afraid?

"Our help is the name of the Lord who made heaven and earth.

"Behold, he that keepeth Israel shall neither slumber nor sleep. . . .

"The Lord is my rock and my fortress and my deliverer.

"The Lord is nigh unto all that call upon him.
"The Lord is good. Blessed is the man that trusteth in him."

Afterward, restored by the strength of her faith and by the solace of prayer, Mary would have slept. Yet before her eyes had closed upon the darkness, there was a sudden disquiet in the street beyond, a murmur of voices, and then the sound of her dread, a heavy knocking upon the doorposts.

At once, she and Joseph were upon their feet, she to seize the little one from his cradle, prepared to flee with him, Joseph to kindle the saucer-lamp, and to open the door with seemly courtesy. Nor would they reveal such disquiet as would cause them to appear either guilty or afraid.

Yet when they had gazed beyond their own doorsill, they knew only wonder. For in the bright blue moonlight falling upon the silent street, there waited three beautiful white camels laden with brilliant trappings. And at the doorway itself, astonishing to look upon, were three strangers, richly garbed, alien of face and of manner. The eldest, a very old man with white hair and beard, lifted his voice before them, and they perceived that he was neither arrogant nor imperious, but gentle and mild.

"Show us the child, for we have seen his star in the east, and have come to worship him."

Persuaded by the stranger's saintly face and kindly voice, Joseph stood aside and allowed them to enter, to approach the little lad lying quietly in his mother's arms. Whereupon they fell down before him, worshiping, and prayed in an alien tongue.

Afterward, the old man told how it was that they had journeyed for a length of days . . . he, Melchior, a Persian, and his companions . . . Gaspar, the Greek, and Balthasar, the Ethiopian with the gleaming turban and the lean, dark face. All were of the Magi, a priestly cult of an eastern faith which worshiped before a single God and had long foretold the coming of a Savior, the Christ, to the world. Each year they searched the skies, in the season of winter, for the promised star. And when at last they beheld in the firmament the fulfillment of their ancient prophecy, they had set forth together, that they might seek the child beneath its light.

Mary uttered no word, being dazed by the unreality of that which had come to pass . . . the strange and resplendent Magi in adoration before her little son, the radiance of the lamp flashing upon their jewels, their richly ornamented robes, the deep blue moonlight streaming through the doorway from the quiet street. Melchior, she perceived, was not unlike Simeon, bowed beneath the weight of as many years, with the same high look of holiness upon his face, the same humble reverence in his eyes. With thin, aged hands he held forth his gift for the little lad, the traditional offering to kings, a casket of gold.

Gaspar, the Greek, was so youthful as to be beardless, lithe of limb, ruddy of cheek. The gift of his hands was costly frankincense, a gum resin which dripped like amber tears from the tree that bore it and gave forth a fragrance of great sweetness when burned as an offering to the Lord, being a symbol of prayer, and of divinity.

Then Balthasar, the Ethiopian, dark and bearded and strange, knelt and laid before the little child an offering of myrrh, gum from an eastern thorn tree which, like frankincense, was both fragrant and costly, yet its use was in the wrappings of the tomb. And, knowing this, Mary shrank from the sight, for Balthasar, a dark figure with myrrh in his hands, seemed the very shadow of death.

Then, as suddenly as they had come, the Magi departed, their dark and alien faces and jeweled robes fading into the shadows, merging with the silence and with the night, the soft hypnotic sound of their camel bells lingering upon the moonlight street as in a dream.

"Now, surely, when they have borne word of us before the king . . ." Mary began, in fear.

"The wisdom of the Magi is known to all," Joseph answered, quietly. "Thus Herod's guile was not concealed from their eyes."

They returned to their bed mats, yet Mary was without peace. Nor would she abandon her son to his cradle, but held his soft little body within her arms, listening to his tender breathing, praying that no soldier of Herod would draw rein before their door. The length of an hour was passed in silence. A cloud rose up and obscured the moon, filling the night with blackness.

Then, suddenly, Mary heard her name on the lips of her husband. She roused quickly, answering him through the stillness.

"As I slept, I dreamed," he whispered, "and one came to me saying that the Magi, being filled with distrust of Herod, will not return to him. Thus his anger will fall upon all of Bethlehem, and he will seek us in every house and street. For this cause, we are to rise in this very hour and go forth to Egypt, that the life of our little one may be spared."

"Yes, truly . . ." The girl rose swiftly, obediently, her heart filled with unvoiced gratitude, knowing it was in her husband's slumber that the Lord had made known His will to them.

They lighted no lamp, lest its gleam cast attention upon their departure. Hastily, in the dimness and silence, they girded themselves for the journey, whispering their words so as not to awaken the little lad, or make their flight known to their neighbors. There were but few things to be made ready, they possessed so little of goods, yet it was known to them that they would require full measures of water and food to sustain their crossing of the desolate wilderness which led to Egypt.

Quietly, Joseph roused the sleeping donkey, gave it drink, heaped upon it their bundles of food and garments, their goatskin bags of water. Mary lifted the child, wrapped him smoothly, rocked him gently in her arms when he stirred and would have wakened. As she awaited her husband, she gazed upon the small, moonlit room with sorrowful eyes. Never again would she sit with the baby Jesus on this doorsill, warmed by the sun. Never again would he slumber in the cradle made sturdy and fair by Joseph's loving hands, the first cradle of her first-born son. Such cradles, being dear to a mother's heart, were at times passed down many generations of first-born sons, but not this cradle, for the child it had sheltered was no ordinary child, and their life together would never be as other lives.

Joseph led the donkey to the door, lifted her upon it, laid the little one in her arms. The moon was shining fitfully, in and out of slow, dark clouds. The streets were empty and still, without so much as the barking of a pariah dog to be heard, and, in this shadowed silence, the feet of the donkey thudded loudly upon the dampened dust. The watchman at the gate was drunken . . . indeed, scarcely looked upon them in his haste to send them forth and return to his wineskin. And presently they had passed beyond the town and were upon the roadway leading down into the plain.

The donkey was strong of body, sure of foot, and went forth as though he found his burden light. He traveled quickly, Joseph's long strides keeping pace with him, their shadows gliding, flat and black, in the moonlit roadway. After a time, another cloud crept upon the moon and quenched it utterly, and the night was of such blackness that the hills were not to be seen against the sky. A vast emptiness spread round and beyond them. In truth, there was no mark of life in all the countryside, save a small and guttering fire where shepherds crouched, watching over their flocks by night in immemorial vigilance.

For a time, they journeyed among the fields and groves and vineyards. Then, as they began the long descent before them, the air appeared warmer, the earth drier, filled with the smell of dust and shattered stone, the breath of the desert.

The way to Egypt was long and desolate, only a little less merciless than Herod's soldiers, a little less to be feared than Herod's wrath. It crossed a vast upheaval of sand and scrub where uncounted rocks rose from the earth and the wind burned like the scorching of flame. Yet, feeling the strong hand of Joseph upon her own, seeing the strong shoulders of Joseph in readiness to bear every burden of herself and her son, Mary gave no thought to fear. Instead, she bowed her head and whispered thanks to God for so wise and tender a husband.

IX.

THERE WAS NO MEANS BY WHICH THEY COULD KNOW WHETHER their flight from Bethlehem had been seen and made known to the soldiers, no means by which they could discover whether these same soldiers now sought them on the roads to Egypt, haven of all persecuted and afraid. Many times, sighting from afar a body of mounted men, they withdrew hastily into the concealing shadow of a rock or the shelter of a cave, remaining hidden until the strangers, only a caravan bound for Jerusalem, had passed. Yet every wanderer halted their flight, rendered them sick with fear: a bearded hermit, a band of goatherds, a lone trader, and once a group of armed men riding swiftly, intently, toward the north, doubtless brigands out of the hills.

Both Mary and Joseph were filled with anxiety lest the little one suffer hurt from the long and desperate journey, the burning days, the chilling nights. After the going down of the sun, they shivered with cold, even in their woolen cloaks, and were driven to seeking shelter among the caves and stones. Often, as Joseph lifted her to the earth, Mary was numb with weariness and her arms, having held her little son hour after hour, were heavy with pain. She huddled against a sun-warmed rock while the donkey searched out tufts of grass and Joseph gathered brushwood for a fire small enough to be quenched quickly, with handfuls of sand, should any be seen to approach. Together they sat by the thin crackle of flame, seeking to warm themselves in its feeble radiance, drank of the stale water in the skin, shared what was left to them of the crumbling bread.

Day upon day they traveled thus through the barren and stony waste, with the sun burning out of an unclouded sky into the dry and sanded watercourses, the unending hills, the limestone ridges, the vast desert wilderness. Even while Joseph walked beside her, it was known to Mary that he suffered unyielding wretchedness, trudged mile upon mile across the searched earth, his feet scorched with its burning, the skin broken to bleeding. His breath came hoarsely, and sweat streamed upon his face. His body was drenched with it, his mouth parched and cracked by wind and sun, even as her own.

In truth, Mary suffered bitterly from the hurried journey. Her delicate skin was blistered by the unsparing heat, her eyes stabbed with pain, and the hours of ceaseless riding, bearing the little child in her arms, brought upon her a torment not to be told. She had known barely sixteen years of life, yet it seemed to her that a century had passed since the night in the stable by the inn.

Each time her little son uttered a sound, she gazed at him fearfully, lest she find him ill or in pain. Yet throughout the length of the journey, it was as though its misery were unknown to him, as though he were impervious to the merciless sun, the fiery wind, the chilling cold. He slept and was fed and slept again and seemed, even as she watched upon him with love and anxiety and unvoiced prayer, to thrive before her eyes.

In the beginning, she and Joseph had sought to cheer and sustain one another, speaking hopefully of Egypt, pointing out certain things perceived from afar: a bird strangely colored, a gazelle bounding from sight among the rocks, a hermit's cave. But, as one day of wretchedness followed another, there seemed no strength left to them beyond that which was needed for their desperate plodding across the last miles of the wilderness. At times, the donkey struggled as though mired deep in sand, and Joseph strove beside him, his face pale and dazed, his eyes unseeing. The journey became an evil dream in which they moved through a red mist of heat that closed out the world, filled their ears with a strange persistent ringing, slashed their eyes with pain.

Once, hastening into a dry watercourse to avoid meeting a caravan, they crashed through thornbrush which tore at their garments, rent their flesh. Coming forth, on the opposite side, tormented by sun, assailed by thorns, choked with dust, they perceived a thinly marked path among the rocks, such as might be wrought by the feet of donkeys traveling, year after year, in single file, or by goats driven day upon day to the same browsing grounds. The sun was low in the sky, so that only a few reddened shafts remained of its light, slanting between black and broken rocks with a glow eerie and unreal. For a time they followed the faintly measured trail but, instead of returning to the broader way, it twisted for a space among the shattered rocks and led them yet deeper into the fastness and loneliness.

"Darkness will soon be upon us," said Joseph, wearily, "and here among the rocks . . . yes, truly, we shall be safe throughout the night."

Mary made no answer. Spent by fear, by days of travel, she felt that the pain of dismounting and striving to walk across sand and stones would be greater than the pain of passing the night going forward on the back of the donkey. Yet it might be that in some sheltered place, away from the chill of darkness, with bread and a small fire and a length of uncluttered earth upon which to stretch her weary body, she would know rest. She was thirsty beyond the telling yet, seeing that the skin held only a small portion of water, she said to herself that this must be given to Joseph, for surely he had the harder lot, walking so great a distance in both haste and desperation.

They had passed around a great rock when suddenly, from the strengthening shadows, there leaped the figure of a man who, even in the dim light, appeared more than ordinarily wretched and unkempt. For all his size, seeing that he was huge beyond other men, he landed upon his feet with the lightness of a great cat, barring the trail before them, his thick hand closed meaningly upon the hilt of the dagger at his waist.

Mary's arms tightened convulsively about the small, soft body of her son while Joseph, holding his countenance impassive and fearless, halted the donkey and, lifting his head, gazed fully into the face of the stranger. For a moment, there was no sound. Then, with unhurried dignity, Joseph spoke.

"Peace to you, brother."

The man made no answer, but the look of wariness with which he had regarded them appeared to depart from his face. His small and narrow eyes moved from the silent girl to the child in her arms, passed swiftly over the donkey in the manner of one accustomed to reckoning the worth of any caravan, however humble, and returned to rest upon the tall and guarded figure of Joseph. Suddenly, he threw back his great shaggy head and uttered a strange, wolflike howl which echoed along the rocks and out across the sands, and lost itself in the desolate waste. It was the cry of a deaf-mute, wild and lonely and terrible. A shudder chilled Mary's heart as she listened, yet afterward she ceased to be afraid for, with a curt gesture, the man stood aside and motioned them forward, along the trail.

Joseph sought to comfort her as they traveled, his great hand laid gently upon her arm. Darkness had fallen, and no man could say what peril awaited them in the barren loneliness beyond, but peril itself seemed more to be desired than the presence of this powerful creature of the wilds. Mary felt now that the donkey was choosing his way with uncommon caution, sensed that Joseph was holding tight to the lead-strap, that he was peering intently ahead, to the great rocks which loomed suddenly against the pale green of the sky.

Presently the ears of the donkey lifted and his small steps quickened as, with unfailing instinct, he sensed the presence of living water. Then, as they passed around a mighty boulder, they came upon a watch fire shrunken to coals which burned with a red, unwavering brilliance into the chill of night. Thin wisps of smoke drifted upward and were lost in darkness. Some brushwood was heaped nearby, as though for a leisurely feeding of the fire through the long hours before dawn. The camp of the deaf-mute, they thought, and had no wish to linger beside it, for all their weariness, and for all its warmth.

In another moment, they would have passed it by, yet suddenly shadows seemed to spring forth from the earth, and they were in the midst of a company of men, all with the same wild and ragged look of the deaf-mute. And now they were aware that the wolflike cry had been a sign to these strangers of their coming.

Joseph halted the donkey quickly, knowing himself helpless against such numbers, his only defense the strength of his courage and perception. Mary's heart thudded with terror and though a wind was rising, edged and cold, sweat gathered in thickened drops upon her forehead. Yet she perceived, gazing into the rough faces of the men, less of hostility than of curiosity. One, a great hairy creature, dark of skin and black of eyes, detached himself from the band and came forward, speaking to Joseph with the ancient words of those who dwell in tents.

"From wherever you come, O stranger, be welcome here!"

Relief assailed the girl so sharply that she caught her breath with a gasp like one in pain. Moving quickly, Joseph was at

77

her side, murmuring reasoning, consoling words in her ear. "In truth they are robbers, yet seeing that we bear neither goods nor gold . . ."

Then the leader of the band, refraining in the manner of the desert from looking upon her face, spoke again.

"To you, brother, and to your wife and your son do we offer our fire, our food . . . yea, and our strength for your defense, should it be required before the dawn."

"Then it is known to you," asked Joseph, courteously, "that I, too, am one of the hunted?"

"More than once we have observed your skill in eluding those whom you had no wish to meet. And so, seeing that we share a common peril, let us also share a common fire, a common feast."

Whereupon he turned his head and uttered words in an alien tongue. The men hastened to do that which he had commanded them to do. Some turned to the baking of bread upon the stones. Others went forth into the darkness and returned bearing a whole roast sheep from a cooking pit a little distance away. Mary gazed with swift hunger upon the meat and, afterward, with mild curiosity, wondering from what distant flock it had been stolen, from what measure of distance it had been borne to this place.

Joseph lifted her from the back of the donkey and spread his cloak for her beside a rock still warm with the heat of noontide. She rested there, apart from the others, and fed her child. The donkey had not been mistaken. A little way beyond the fire was a well more than half filled with water. And when she had done with drinking from the suddenly bulging skin, she bathed from herself and her little one some of the dust and wretchedness of the journey. After a time, a portion of the roast flesh and newly baked bread was borne to her in the hands of Joseph. She ate hungrily, rested, and knew peace.

It was not the way of the wilderness to ask from whence a

stranger came, the direction of his flight, or the nature of his offense. In the manner of brothers, the men sat about the fire, dipping together into the food, their voices a distant murmur of contentment. They might have been a gathering of pious Jews on their way to the Passover, save that their faces reflected other blood. Large, sinewy, powerfully formed, they were like the desert itself in their look of endurance, in ruthlessness and might.

Knowing, after a time, the yearning to sleep, Mary settled herself against the warmth of the rock, her eyes half closed to the strange scene before her, the rough faces of the men, their beards and shaggy hair, their knotted fists lighted by the redness of the fire. And, as she reflected upon these things, growing yet more drowsy, she was startled by the sound of an urgent whisper.

"I would look upon your babe. . . ."

At once, she roused, bewildered and frightened, seeing nothing. Then, aware of a movement beside her, she turned and beheld a small lad five or six years of age. He was also shaggy of head, unclean, and somewhat ragged, yet his great black eyes were humble, and filled with pleading.

"I would look upon your babe. . . ."

He drew nearer and clutched at her cloak with a grimy brown hand, awaiting her trustfully, and when she had recovered from the astonishment upon her, the heart of Mary yearned toward him . . . so small and gentle a child in so vast and harsh a wilderness. Swiftly the thought came to her: Is his mother here also? Yet she perceived no movement in the shadows behind him, nor was it to be thought that the men would have set their hands to the roasting of the meat, the baking of the bread, had there been women within the camp.

Quietly, she placed her little son upon her knee where, roused briefly from slumber, he stirred once, and opening his eyes, looked upward with a babe's smiling yawn.

With indrawn breath, the small lad went down on his knees beside Mary and stared intently at the child, saying no word. Then, suddenly, he leaped up and fled to the watch fire, casting himself upon the leader of the robber band.

"A babe, my father!" he cried, in vast excitement. "Would you wish to look upon it also?"

The man received him with gruff gentleness and, turning to Joseph, said, "It is my first-born son, whom we call the Little Robber, but one day to be a big robber . . . a *great* robber, ha?" And he laughed with unconcealed pleasure, rumpling the child's black hair. In sudden tenderness, he said, "He has a fondness for small creatures, this one . . . for baby jackals and birds and lambs, and all tiny things. Yet until this night, he has never beheld a baby man."

With his voice yet lower, the man went on, "His mother also had a fondness for small creatures, being gentle of heart, even though a slave girl. It was for the Little Robber that she gave her life, seeing that when one of the lions would have slain him, she ran to his side and fended off the beast until her cries brought us forth to her defense. Behold, the mark of the lion yet remains. . . ." And he turned the child's head with his brawny hand, so that the firelight fell upon a thin, crescent-shaped scar from his temple to his jaw.

Then, released, the little lad hastened again to Mary's side, and sat staring at her with round black eyes, now and then bending to peer, enchanted, at the sleeping babe. A little time later, she felt him slump against her and, looking down, perceived that he was deep in slumber, one hand clutching the fabric of her skirt. Tenderly, she drew her cloak about him, that he might be shielded from the cold.

She wondered whether he recalled the girl who had given her life for him, and knew compassion for the valiant little slave who was perhaps younger than she, and who must have brought forth her first-born as she had done, with neither the aid nor the comfort of any woman, and in a shelter yet humbler than the stable behind the inn. In truth, she was a girl of beauty if the Little Robber resembled her, for his skin possessed the tawny loveliness of a ripened apricot, his eyes were heavily lashed, his face warm with sweetness. She pitied the child for the loneliness of his life and the wretchedness of his lot, yet she was aware that his father regarded him tenderly, and that he bore a deep love for this huge, lawless man. Whether or not the slave girl had borne love for this man also was a thing unknown, not even to be surmised, since it was not for such a one to choose who should father her children.

One after another, the men drew apart from the fire, rolled themselves in cloaks upon the sanded earth, and slept. Save for the faint sputter of coals, and the crying of jackals beyond in the hilly darkness, there was no sound. Then the night wind rose, lashing the wilderness under a glittering pageantry of stars, and presently, full of the wild beauty of this desolate place, Mary slept also.

When she awakened, a little past dawn, the men had vanished into the hills, leaving behind only the deaf-mute and the child. She and Joseph ate and drank, filled their waterskins afresh, and made ready to set forth. As she waited beside the donkey, the Little Robber came running from some hidden place beyond the rocks, bearing in his hand that which gleamed and glittered in the radiance of the morning sun.

"Behold," he said, breathlessly, "I would trade it for your little one. It is of great worth, my father has said. . . ."

And he held forth a necklace, an intricate blending of gold and jewels which must have been the work of some craftsman's heart, even of his life. Mary shuddered, gazing upon it, wondering in what merciless and bloody raid it had come to the hand of the robber chief.

"If . . . if this one is too small a price, there are yet more," said the little lad, with eagerness. Tenderly, he touched the folds in which the child of Mary slumbered, stroking them softly, filled with dreaming. "Truly, he shall remain with me always, and I will guard him with my life, and we shall be as brothers throughout the length of our days. . . ."

She laid one hand against the tender cheek, halting the words, taking care not to bruise his hopes too suddenly or with harshness.

"My babe is so very small," she said, gently, "that he could not live without his mother to give him care. . . ."

The Little Robber listened solemnly as she spoke and, in the end, received her words with the fatalism of desert peoples, blinking tears from the great dark eyes which, only a moment earlier, had been agleam with eagerness. And, as she and Joseph set forth again upon their journey, Mary looked back and perceived the child standing sorrowfully in the shadow of a great rock, the necklace dangling from his small brown hands, its jewels become fire in the brightness of the risen sun.

X.

THAT MORNING, AWAKENING IN HER MOTHER'S HOUSE, IT WAS
as if she were again a young and untroubled girl. Mary lay
on her bed mat in silence and tranquillity, savoring the sight
of things remembered and cherished and thus dear within her
heart. To this deep-silled window she had opened her eyes
through all the years of her growing up, watching as now,
while a ragged cloud edged across the fair blue sky beyond it.
After a time, she turned her head and gazed about the room,
from the smoky beams of the ceiling to the cleanly floor, from
the shelf arranged with lamps and bowls and utensils of the
house, the loom, the jars, the wedding chest to the sight of
her husband sleeping in the dimness, and beyond, on a little
bed mat of his own, the child Jesus, now past the second year
of his life.

On the day before, at a certain sunset hour, they had returned to Galilee, journeying from Egypt peacefully, with
neither fear nor haste. Yet they did not cease to recall the
bitterness and terror of their flight from Bethlehem after the
visit of the Magi, or the anguish from which this flight had
spared them. For on the same morning, the soldiers of Herod
swept into Bethlehem and, by command of their king, had
slain every babe less than two years of age. There was but a
small number of such little ones and all lay dead within the
space of an hour. Thus Herod brooded no longer upon the

prophecy, but rejoiced in his own deed, believing it had delivered his throne from the child of the star.

In Egypt they dwelt quietly and without peril while Joseph labored at his trade and Mary tended their small house and cared for the little lad. After the manner of all good Jewish mothers, she kept him beside her as she prayed, that he might be aware, even from the days of his babyhood, of the presence of the Lord in their lives. In truth, she taught him to feel this presence in the simplest portions of their life. "Behold, my babe, the cooling rain which God has sent to us this day . . . the little flower . . . the merry bird upon the branch. . . ." His daily bread, she made known to him, was a gift of God, likewise his sleep, the little tunic he wore, the wind of the morning, the stars at night. And the first words he uttered, learned from her patient and gentle lips, were those of the Jewish profession of faith: "Hear, O Israel, the Lord our God is one God. . . ."

Knowing content in the immeasurable love of her husband and the sweet presence of her little son, Mary suffered no loneliness. Yet, in the season of springtime, her heart turned back with homesick yearning to the fair province of Galilee, its uncounted groves and blossoming hillsides and sown fields. Thus she awoke with a sense of deliverance on a certain night, hearing Joseph call to her that which had come to him in a dream: "*Arise and take the child and the mother and return to Israel, for he is dead who sought the life of the child.*"

Herod had come to an end befitting his life, his body as befouled as the heart within it, his latter days a frenzy of unabating terror and pain. Afterward, according to his will, the empire was divided among his sons, broken into three portions. Thus Herod Antipas, the son who received Galilee, would rule it, not as a king, but as a prince inferior and without eminence, a tetrarch.

"In Galilee," said Joseph, thoughtfully, "surely we shall

know peace . . . for who is it that would look upon the lad with suspicion now? Though a length of more than two years has passed, none has risen to say from whence came the couple with a promised child, to offer their names, or the names of their village. In truth, there was a day when both Bethlehem and Jerusalem heard talk of a newborn Messiah, the tale of the shepherds, word of Simeon and Hannah, and of the Magi from the east. Now, such tales are of the past, obscure and only half recalled."

"Not even our brethren know of them," Mary answered.

"Nor must they!" he answered quickly. "Keep these matters within your own heart, voicing them not even before Mary Cleophas, lest her lively tongue bear them to other doorsills . . . lest, in time, it be whispered to the new Herod that the child of promise still lives and may be found in Nazareth of Galilee."

"I shall utter no word of it," said Mary, and swift terror assailed her as she thought of the peril to her son, were the truth made known. Thus they let it be said by those of Nazareth that Joseph had journeyed forth, first to Jerusalem and thence to Egypt, seeking higher wages but, having grown homesick at last, had returned to his own village, there to be content with his lot. The little lad, born in this time, was received in a manner both tender and loving, hailed by all of Nazareth for his unusual beauty and sweetness of manner.

Now, at peace in the morning light, Mary pondered upon these things until, hearing Joseph stir, she rose and set about beginning a new day. Even though the early rains are past, she said to herself, there is yet time for planting and growing such a garden as I once tended for the needs of my mother and myself. . . . With money carefully hoarded against the day of their return, they would buy a few fowls, some sheep, a pair of brown goats, that the child might have milk, warm and strengthening, with each day. Joseph would again open a shop, and those of the village, regarding him with affection and esteem, would bestow upon him their welcome and their custom. They would live a life simple and serene, close to God and to one another, observing the law in the manner of all devout Jewish people, teaching their son to love and observe it also, keeping the holy secret until God Himself should choose to reveal it before the world.

In her marriage to Joseph she was utterly content, for no measure of the wonder had departed from it. Nor was it unknown to her that save for his tender protection, his strength and quiet wisdom, neither she nor her son would have survived the perils and sorrows of their years together. By the striving of his toil-stained hands and the streaming sweat of his body, he had earned bread and shelter for her, and for the son he loved as his own.

"Both you and Jesus shall be a sacred trust to me all the days of my life," he told her, and there rose up between them the wonder, the unfailing love, the shared remembrances.

Thus the seasons came and went, and the little lad grew sturdy, knowing neither frailty nor illness throughout the years of his childhood, learning to walk in the paths of the Lord. After the way of Jewish mothers, Mary taught him his first simple prayers and verses of scripture, then the Ten Commandments, and certain of the psalms.

As every child, he gazed with wondering eyes upon the vast world before him, hastening to ask her of those matters which troubled or perplexed him.

With all other sons of the village, he learned to obey the word of his parents, to trust in their wisdom and judgment, look to them with respect, and share with them the tasks of the household. Thus, when he was five, he was given the duty of helping to care for the sheep and lambs. Each morning, when they had done with drinking, he set forth with them, leading them through the dust of the street to the common pasture beyond the village. Yet it was with a wrench at her heart that Mary saw this come about, for until now, they had passed all his waking hours together. As she plodded, barefoot, in the loam of the garden, bent to the weary task of planting, he was at her side, gazing intently upon the seeds she pressed within his hand, moved to wonder by the thought that, one day, they would be melons for the table, or for the market a little distance away.

Within the house, he witnessed her baking of the daily bread, marveling as she filled the measure with meal and afterward mixed into it, as leaven, a lump of stale and soured dough. Hour upon hour, he watched while his mother dealt with the tasks of the day, bringing forth numberless questions while she answered him gravely and well.

"Wherefore do you wash the scrap of new cloth before you use it for the mending of my tunic? Surely the scrap is clean, seeing that it has not been worn."

She smiled.

"I wash it that it may be shrunken, even as the other. If this were not done, then the new cloth would shrink away from the old when they are washed together, and thus make larger than ever the tear that was mended."

On a certain morning, he asked, mindful and wondering, "Wherefore do you hasten with the washing of the garments this day?"

"I would have them dry before the rain has fallen."

"Will the rain come soon?"

"Yes, truly, my child."

"How is this known to you, Mother?"

She straightened her weary young body, pushed thick, damp hair from her forehead with a wet and reddened hand. Then, seating herself upon one of the benches and taking her son upon her knees, she began to teach him in the fashion of loving mothers.

"This morning, the sunrise was both red and clouded . . . and when this comes to pass, foul weather awaits us. If the wind of the south is blowing, crossing the sands of the desert, the day will be very hot. At eventide, a cloud rising dark in the west means that rain will fall in but a little time. Yet if the sunset is red, then truly, the hours to come will be fair."

"How is it that a red sunset means a fair day, Mother?"

"It is God's sign in the sky."

Always he was at her side when she went forth upon some journey of mercy, bearing gruel for the aged, a healing draught for the ill, the comfort of words for the sorrowing. They shared a great compassion for all who suffered, and thus, to their outstretched hands crept small forlorn puppies shaking with hunger, lambs too weak to follow the flock, fledglings fallen from the nest, all manner of spent and defenseless creatures. And, as they shared a likeness of the spirit, so did they share a likeness of the flesh . . . the same swift lifting of the head, the same clear-eyed look from beneath thick black lashes, the same sweetness of countenance and gracious manner of speech.

At times, when they had gone forth from the village for the gathering of meadow greens, he would gaze searchingly at the birds among the branches.

"How is it that they find bread, Mother?"

"God feeds them in his own way, my child."

He would sit in the tall grasses as quietly as a little hare, while she revealed to his eyes certain small creatures of the wilds . . . tiny foxes tumbling before a den, fledglings seeking morsels from the beaks of their mother, bees bearing sweetness to a hive in the rocks.

He looked upon the meadow grasses, perceiving their delicate burden of seeds, their burnished rippling in the wind. He marveled at the reeds of the marshes which, though of great height, were so pliant as to lie flat before the wind and to rise again, unbroken, when it had passed. He rejoiced in the flowers, gazing with wonder upon the anemones arrayed in a thousand shades of radiant color against the hills.

"How is it that they have come forth from the earth, with no gardener to tend them?"

"God is their gardener, my son."

Once, as they returned to the village, burdened by that which they had gathered, he perceived slaves toiling along the great road in the plain below, the caravan way ravaged by the early rains, and by the washings of the hillsides. Whereupon the lad turned to his mother, asking, "What is it that they do?"

Shielding her eyes from the brightness of the sun, Mary beheld the laborers cleansing and mending the scars of the winter season.

"They are preparing the way," she said, slowly, "a thing done only for a traveler of rank . . . a Roman noble, perhaps, or a foreign king."

Quietly she waited, that he might behold what passed below, knowing he found wonder in whatever his eyes beheld, heard with eagerness all that was spoken before him.

"Your child possesses wisdom beyond his years," the elders said to her. "He should go forth even now to the learning of the law."

Every son of Nazareth who had come to the sixth year of his life was obliged to attend the synagogue school, a matter enforced by a council of elders sternly aware of the duty before them. James and Joses and Simon, the sons of Cleophas, looked upon the school with distaste, but with Jesus, seeing that he had a love of learning, it was otherwise. In truth, it was no easy thing for him to await the Sabbath of his presentation.

On that day, he washed himself carefully, and Mary put upon his sturdy little body the new tunic she had woven for this hour. She herself was clad in her Sabbath dress and sandals, a thin veil, and the cherished girdle of her betrothal. With the lad between them, she and Joseph set out through the grave hush of the holy morning, Joseph wearing a girdled tunic which appeared uncommonly fair in contrast to his brown face and great brown hands. They made their way slowly, quietly, along streets patterned with sun and shadow, empty save for other families not unlike their own, and ascended the synagogue steps at last. The eyes of Jesus were big with wonder, seeking out the master, beholding the dignity of his beard, his long black tunic, his prayer shawl. According to the duty of a mother, Mary led him forward.

"My first-born . . ." she began, and a tremor seized upon her voice.

The rabbi nodded.

"Jesus, son of Joseph the carpenter," he answered, in seemly affirmation.

Mary said no word. Gently, Joseph motioned the lad to go with the master, that he might take his place among the other pupils. It was the first time in his life for him to be given to the hands of a stranger and, for a moment, he drew back, clinging to his mother's fingers. Then, loosing his hold upon her, he lifted his small shoulders and went forth from her side, and from the years of his babyhood.

With the coming of another day, he set out for the first of his lessons, and a great loneliness came upon her. Yet, with the hour of noonday, he hastened within, breathless for having run such a measure of distance, his voice filled with excitement. Mary bore food to the table, Joseph came forth from his shop, and while they broke their bread together, they heard what the lad would say of the morning . . . how it was that the pupils sat on rows of mats before the master's platform, how Joses, becoming unruly and inattentive, had felt the smart of the rabbi's stick. With a smile rich in remembrance,

Joseph gazed across the board into Mary's eyes. And she perceived that his thoughts were of another school, another sharply wielded stick. To his ears rose again the shrill voices of children learning to recite from memory, and in unison, the old laws and history tales, the prophecies and psalms. And perhaps there came to him also the feel of a stylus in a small and awkward hand, striving to copy a letter from a scroll.

With each day that passed, the lad's love of learning appeared to strengthen, and it was known throughout Nazareth that in the synagogue school none excelled Jesus, son of Joseph the carpenter. In body also he was strengthened, fleet at running, tireless in his climbing of the hills. Yet, since he possessed ready laughter, was swift in compassion and understanding, he roused neither rivalry nor resentment in the hearts of those about him. Lads other than his brethren joined him and they were merry together, going forth with the flocks, turning to the games of boyhood, reciting their lessons, at times speaking gravely, and with wonder, of the old prophecies.

". . . said that he will come suddenly, with only a voice crying in the wilderness to go before him. . . ."

And, in their words, Mary heard the same syllables of awe which had come upon her in her childhood, as she listened to the teachings of Zacharias. Pain assailed her now, as she thought of the gentle priest, and of Elizabeth the beloved, both dead of fever, in the days when she and Joseph dwelt with the child in Egypt.

Of their illness and dying, Mary Cleophas had told her all. The voice of the Lord had come to him, Zacharias declared, even as his life ebbed from him, commanding that he send forth his son, the little John, not with those of his kindred, but into the care of the Essenes, the strange and austere holy men on the shore of the Dead Sea.

Mary thought many times of the lad, now past the seventh

year of his life, clad in the hair garments of the brotherhood, sharing their spare and frugal meals, dwelling amid the desert silences, unaware of any earthly brethren of his own. Was she never to behold his face again? It was a matter written on a page yet unrolled, even as the words of Simeon, of Hannah, of the shepherds and the messenger of the Lord.

"These things God will reveal in His own time," Joseph told her simply.

That morning he had gone forth with Cleophas to the market at Lydda, a little distance away. The sight of his shop, empty and utterly silent, was akin to loneliness itself, and gazing upon it, Mary knew the sense of desolation which came to her each time they were parted, one from the other. Beyond, the sky was darkened by heavy clouds, and there hovered upon the village an air of quiet sadness presaging the autumn rains.

In the early darkness, she kindled a lamp and set it in a niche in the wall. Soon thereafter, as she and Jesus awaited the sound of Joseph's coming, the rain began its falling. Wearied with the labors of the day, she seated herself near the hearth, on one of the low stools. Whereupon the lad came to her and sat at her feet and, in a manner wholly his own, leaned his head against her. The lamp flame wavered in the gusts, casting shadows upon the room, and suddenly it appeared to her that the face of Simeon was among them, that the words of Simeon were murmured upon the rising wind. *"And . . . thine . . . own . . . soul . . . a . . . sword . . . shall . . . pierce. . . ."* Thus Mary shuddered and drew the lad nearer to her side.

She was aware, after the way of mothers, that already he had begun to outgrow his need of her. No longer did he waken her at night with the child's cry "I thirst!" but rose softly in the darkness, and made his way to the water jar, that he might drink. Even before he went forth to his schooling, he had sought to wash and garb himself, had clumsily smoothed his hair.

She perceived him assuming, without his own knowledge, an authority among the lads of the village, even those of years greater than his own. Such authority, being his destiny, would bear him far beyond the walls of Nazareth, far beyond her sight.

The shadows moved in the dimness, the yellow lamplight gleamed upon his rumpled black head, the sweet brown softness of his childish neck. Rain fell steadily through the risen wind, beating upon the rooftop, the garden, the courtyard, the narrow street. The lad moved closer within the warm, gentle curve of her arm and Mary perceived that his eyes were heavy with slumber.

"Father in heaven," she prayed silently, "wherever Thy will shall lead him, there let me also abide."

XI.

REACHING THE AGE OF TWELVE, A SON OF GALILEE BECAME A son of the law, being bound to know and keep it in the manner of all worthy Jews, going forth with his elders each year to the great feast of the Passover in the holy city of Jerusalem.

The tale of the Passover was known to Jewish children from the earliest years of their lives. Mary had told it many times to her son, bringing before his eyes the lordly figure of the noble young Moses who had been called an Egyptian prince, but who turned from all ease of life, that he might lead his people out of their bondage to the Egyptian ruler.

For, enslaved, they were cruelly bound, lashed and starved and set upon like pariah dogs. Thus Moses went before the Pharaoh, crying out in the name of the Lord, "Let my people go. . . ." Yet it was not until the Pharaoh and all of his land had been afflicted by ten great plagues that he would assent. And the tenth plague was the death of the first-born sons of Egypt.

For the Lord said, "Every house of Israel shall slay a lamb in the evening of a certain day, and with its blood shall mark the doorposts of the houses wherein they eat it. And ye shall eat the flesh of the lamb that night, roast with fire, and with bitter herbs. And ye shall eat it in haste. It is the feast of the Lord's passover.

"For this night I shall smite the first-born sons of Egypt, yet when I see the blood on the doorposts of the houses of the children of Israel, I will pass over them, and the plague shall not be upon them or their children.

"And this night shall be unto you a memorial, and ye shall keep it with a feast unto the Lord throughout your generations. . . ."

Whereupon it was done as the Lord had said. And when the first-born sons of the Egyptians were smitten with death, the heart of the Pharaoh was filled with a great fear, and he said unto Moses, "Rise up and get you forth, both you and the children of Israel. . . ."

And Moses led his people forth from Egypt, departing with such a measure of haste that there was no time to accomplish the baking of their bread, which was not risen. Thus they set out with their kneading troughs upon their shoulders. And, afterward, when they had grown hungry, and had baked and eaten of the unleavened bread, it became to them, like the eating of the lamb, ever a symbol of their liberation, and of their faith.

Each year thereafter, to keep the Passover, a pure white lamb was slain and offered by each family on the altar of God, in humble gratefulness for their deliverance, and the flesh was eaten with bitter herbs and unleavened bread in memory of the ancient flight out of bondage. Yet since it was not permitted that a lamb be slain and sacrificed by any save the priests of the great temple, it was necessary for each man to make the journey to Jerusalem, that this might be accomplished. All went forth, save those ill or enfeebled or yet too young to be bound by the words of the law.

The time of the Passover was chosen in accordance with the waxing of the moon, so that those who made the long pilgrimage to the holy city might have the radiance of a full moon to light their way through the deep valleys and along the tortuous paths among the hills, for the spreading forth of their bed mats, the gathering of brushwood for their fires.

Many days were spent by the women of Nazareth in making ready for the journey, and since his first Passover was of no small consequence in the life of a Jewish lad, the son of Mary was filled with joyous excitement. She had woven a new tunic for his wearing, laboring until late at night, the radiance of the lamp touching and glorifying her soft dark hair, the serene and lovely lines of her face, the swift movements of her hands. Carefully she and Joseph had garnered money against the coming of spring, so that now they possessed coins for the purchase of the slain lamb, for tithes such as all Jewish families bore to the temple, and for the buying of sandals for Jesus. In her baskets, she laid fruit and nuts to be eaten on the journey, vegetables plucked in her own garden, honey, olive oil, flour, and a measure of parched barley.

Early on a certain fair morning, the travelers assembled in the market place and, when all had come, set forth together in a long and joyous processional led by the elders of the village.

There were men as well as beasts laden with burdens, men who bore staves to help them upon their way, women who rode while a husband or son led the donkey upon which they sat, other women like Mary Cleophas who walked and was merry and knew no weariness, even though she bore in her arms a babe only a little past the first month of life. For a time, even those who could not make the journey went forth with the travelers, halting a little way beyond Nazareth to bid them farewell, to linger, gazing after them with unconcealed yearning . . . little ones, women heavy with children yet unborn, men aged and infirm, such as the lame cobbler who, until the family of Joseph returned, would tend their goats and sheep and fowls.

For the pilgrims, it was a season of merriment, a joyous release from labor. The men called to one another in voices easy and brotherly, the light tones of the women were mingled in lively words. Children ran from the line and returned to it again, led forth by many wonders, the nest of a bird, the flight of a bee, the colors of an uncommon flower.

Spring in Galilee possessed a loveliness beyond the telling. In truth, the plain which lay before them was not unlike some garden of the Lord, glorified with anemones of a thousand hues, with tender winds and spice-laden fragrances, new grasses, the flowering boughs of the olives and the almonds.

Yet, in that moment, Mary was both grave and silent, recalling another journey, when she and Joseph had traveled to Bethlehem, the weariness she had known on the snowswept heights near Jerusalem, the pain and the despair. And there came to her thoughts also the disquieted night when she and Joseph had set out for Egypt, driven by terror, the hoofs of the donkey thudding in the darkness, clattering upon the stony heights, struggling in the sanded depths of the wilderness. Then she had held in her arms a babe who was now a son of the law bound for his first keeping of the Passover. She watched him mingling with the other lads, falling back beside her to smile with her over some light word or jest, matching his stride with that of Joseph as he brought forth eager questions and received thoughtful answers. Her face was tender as she gazed upon him, and her heart went forth in gratitude before the Lord for so comely a son, so rich a blessing. Often her pride in his wisdom, his courage, and gentleness filled her with the yearning to speak, to cry out before all of Nazareth that he was no peasant child but the promised Savior, the Messiah. Yet the counsel of her husband and the guidance of God restrained her, and thus she concealed these thoughts within her heart.

After a time, she heard the voice of her son lifted in astonishment.

"Is it indeed true that we are to cross Samaria?"

And when Joseph nodded, he went on, perplexed and wondering.

"How is it that we do this thing, seeing that their hearts are hardened against our nation?"

"Since we are great in number, we need have no fear for our own safety," said Joseph. "The way through Samaria is less burdensome than the journey by Jericho, and not so far in distance. Thus it is well that we choose it, even though we are despised in the eyes of those who dwell there."

An older lad, hearing their words, cried out that the Samaritans were a people wholly evil of heart and deed. But Joseph would not have it so.

"Nay," he said, "for there dwells upon the earth no tribe without just and righteous men."

That night they spread their bed mats in an olive grove with the sound of wind in its boughs. The radiance of the moon fell about them, bringing into being the edges of the leaves, the tips of the grasses, the deep shadows of the trees. Long after a dreaming silence had fallen upon the encampment, Mary lay awake, savoring the deep contentment of this hour, knowing the night beautiful beyond other nights, her child and her husband safe in slumber, the presence of the Lord drawn near to them.

She gazed upon the lad lying upon his bed mat in the deep grasses, where he had flung himself in pleasant weariness. Now he slept the sweet slumber of youth, his brown face pillowed upon one arm, his hair a disordered shadow, his face untroubled and serene. And her heart cried out, after the way of mothers, "My son, my son! In but a little time, you will go forth from me, a man. . . ." And it came to her that there might be a night when she would stand alone, gazing upon the white paschal moon, knowing not where he lay, nor what passed within his heart. Yet, she said to herself, such is the lot of mothers, nor is it mine alone.

With morning, they were joined by other gatherings of pilgrims, one from Capernaum, on the beautiful lake to the north. And Mary's heart was warm with pleasure, perceiving among them her openhearted kinswoman, Salome, wife of Zebedee. Others of Nazareth went forth to brethren in the same gathering, and the company halted for a little space in joyous reunion.

Zebedee was a large, easy-mannered fisherman made brown by years of wind and sun, his wife an ample woman light of heart and word, yet possessed of an uncommon wisdom and tenderness. Not since the early years of his childhood had Jesus looked upon their sons, the stalwart and lively James, the gentle John. Between Mary and this second son of Zebedee there was deep affection, and as she embraced him, gazing into his sweet brown face and warm dark eyes, it came to her that their nearness of heart had come about for the reason that he possessed a nature akin to that of Jesus, and to her own.

The lads went forth together and, after a little time, Mary heard their voices mingled in talk of the lake, the fishing boats, the manner of bringing a night's catch into the nets. In truth, she thought, these must fall as tales of wonder upon the ears of her son, seeing that he had never beheld a lake or river, save from a far distance. And she perceived that by the time they had come upon the springs of Beeroth, at the end of the third day, the three lads were such companions of the spirit as do not forget their days together.

The long journey was lightened by the chants of the pilgrims older yet than the pilgrimage itself. *"Our feet shall stand within thy gates, O Jerusalem . . . whither the tribes go up . . . to give thanks unto the name of the Lord. . . ."* Yet, after a time, their early exuberance lost itself in heat and thirst and weariness. The ascent to Jerusalem was no easy thing. In truth, it had become a slow and heavy plodding for all . . . the men and women, their children and their beasts of burden, striving over hills and stones, across barren earth and sanded, among thorns and dusty watercourses, assailed by the merciless burning of the sun. Yes, truly, Mary said to herself, it was not unlike the region of the Little Robber, the wilderness wherein he had been born, wherein he had grown to the years of his manhood . . . if, indeed, he yet lived and had not perished in some raid of death and plunder. By this time, he would have passed his eighteenth year, she thought, and was stirred by a sense of sadness, recalling his small grave face.

And there was another whose image rose before her eyes, against the dust and stones . . . John, the son of Zacharias and Elizabeth, now counted among the Essenes, those who dwelt in the desert that they might prepare the way of the Savior by prayer and fasting and the study of the law.

She thought of him, a lad grown stalwart and brown and strange, sitting down to the common board, the frugal fare, the silence of unsparing discipline . . . going forth to the chosen labors of the brotherhood, the wresting of sustenance from the stony soil, the keeping of herds and flocks and swarms of bees, the learning of skills from those who were craftsmen, the patient tending of those aged and ill . . . giving certain watches of the night to unceasing prayer, to holy thoughts, to the reading of the scrolls by the light of a single flame. Yes, truly, he had become a creature of the wilderness, knowing no world beyond its desolation, its burning dawns and timeless stars and silent, unending hills become as brothers known and beloved in his heart.

The pilgrims were wordless now, wretched with heat and weariness, striving forth with the shuffling sound of feet in sand, the thudding of staves, the clatter of hoofs on stone. Then, suddenly, as they came upon the crest of a certain hill, they beheld Jerusalem. At once, as though by reason of a miracle, the walls and roofs and towers of the holy city rose

100

before them, the golden temple gleaming in the sun, the first thick dark smoke lifted upward on the wind from the altars of the evening sacrifices. Shouts burst forth from the parched throats of the pilgrims as, with their weariness departing from them, their spirits restored, they surged toward the gates of Jerusalem, their voices lifted in the ancient song of rejoicing: *"I was glad when they said unto me . . . Let us go to the house of the Lord. . . ."*

To the House of the Lord she and Joseph had borne the child in the sweetness of an early morning almost twelve years past, and now to the House of the Lord they had returned. The seasons were passing swiftly, bearing them nearer to the destiny of the promised child. Thus she put forth her hand and laid it upon the dark head of her son, as though, by the touch, she might keep him at her side for a little time longer.

XII.

THE STREETS OF THE HOLY CITY WERE THRONGED WITH PIL-
grims, likewise the houses, the inns, the rooftops, even the valleys below, and the hills beyond. Thousands upon thousands
crowded through the gates, the old and the young, the learned
and the untaught, those who were simple peasants and craftsmen, those who dwelt in high houses with slaves at their command. By every street and highroad and bypath they came,
pouring out of the mountains, clambering up from the depths
of the valleys, ascending from the desolation of the wilderness,
that they might sacrifice upon the altar of the Lord.

The Jews who dwelt within Jerusalem received uncounted
numbers within their houses, upon their rooftops, into the
upper rooms which many kept from year to year for those of
the Passover. Such rooms were furnished with bed mats, water
jars, coverlets to shield the slumberer from the chill of night,
a table for the serving of the holy feast. And to seek pay for
hospitality thus given to pilgrims would have been a matter
of shame.

Those with neither friends nor brethren to receive them
turned to the hills and valleys about the city, spreading forth
their encampments here, and along the brook of Kidron . . .
not a stream, but an empty watercourse flooded only in the
seasons of rain. Some slept upon the barren earth, huddled
within woolen cloaks, drawn near to the warmth of their

102

animals. Others spread their bed mats as their nomadic fore-fathers had done, in the shelter of tents or boughs.

A little before they entered the gates of the city, Jesus beheld for the first time the extremity of mortal wretchedness and despair. From some figures gathered near the roadway came a sudden clattering of small wooden bells and a crying out of the fearful words, "Unclean! Unclean!" And, seeking the hand of the lad, Mary said to him gently, "My son, they are lepers. . . ."

It was a scene of misery to sicken the beholder: creatures of rotted flesh, faces with neither lips nor nose, arms without hands, the smell of decay, the stumps of feet, the sight of bones from which all flesh had fallen. Nor were they alone in their wretchedness, for a little distance beyond, one looked upon those blind from birth, those with broken bones, the lame and crippled and deaf, those afflicted with seizures and madness, driven forth with the lepers to beg their bread.

Mary perceived that the smooth young face of her son had paled before the horror of this sight, that his dark eyes had taken on a measure of the sorrow and suffering before him. And she sought to comfort him, saying to him, "Behold, my darling, we shall divide food and coins among these piteous ones. . . ." Yet she knew he took no consolation from the words, that he was grieved to the heart by that which he had looked upon.

At the gates of the city, they perceived the familiar publicans, the hated Jewish taxgatherers who served Rome and defrauded their own people. For while a publican levied upon the goods of a traveler, he increased the lawful sum to his own gain. And should any lift his voice against this injustice, a fine might be laid upon him, his goods seized in the name of the emperor, flogging or imprisonment inflicted upon him.

Yet it was not only in this manner that the Jews were taxed by Rome, but also in the paying of a head tax, meat and bread and salt taxes, a water tax, road tolls and levies from each city and town. The craftsmen who bore their wares to market, the peasants who set forth with the fruits of their acres were halted at every village, stream, and crossroad, required to pay a toll at the booth of some taxgatherer of Tiberius Caesar. And should a man be unable to pay all that was demanded of him, the Romans seized his land, his fields and vineyards, his ox and donkey, destroyed his house, enslaved or imprisoned those within.

It was required also that the Jews pay certain tithes to the great temple, likewise the first fruits of their orchards, vineyards, fields, and flocks . . . these being given to the hands of the High Priest. Goods for worship might be purchased only in the temple market, which was owned by the High Priest's family. Here incense, flour for the shewbread, holy oils, doves and lambs and oxen of sacrifice were sold at any price he found pleasing. And though Roman coin was used in trade, tithes and purchases must be paid in temple shekels. Thus rows of money-changers sat within the temple market, converting the money of the pilgrims into temple coin, and charging, for this, a sum neither rightful nor just.

Yet, seeing that the temple was the house of their God, the Jews paid tithes to it with gladness of heart, and bore many gifts to its gates. It was a structure of utter splendor, its beautiful courts divided by exquisite columns, gates, and stairs.

The vast outer court, roofed with fragrant cedar, was known as the Court of Gentiles, since any might enter here. Around it was a colonnade of fair white marble with a floor of beautifully patterned tile, the place of the temple market.

None save Jews could climb the twelve steps ascending from the Court of Gentiles to the inner temple. On every gate was inscribed for all to behold: *Beyond this point none of the uncircumcised may pass, on pain of death.*

The first court within the gates was the Court of Women by

which they were separated, during the temple services, from their men. A second flight of twelve steps ascended to the Court of Israel, separated by a low balustrade from the Court of Priests.

Within this court were tables for the washing and skinning of the animals of sacrifice, and hooks from which these might be hung. A cistern in the earth beneath furnished water for the washing away of filth and bloodstains.

Beyond the Court of Priests was the holy shrine which none save priests might enter. It was here that Zacharias had stood, casting incense upon the golden altar, when the messenger of the Lord appeared before him.

North of the temple, and so near as to cast its heavy shadow upon the sanctuary of the Lord, rose the uneven stone walls and galleries of the great Antonia Fortress, garrison of Roman troops and Roman might. Stairs and runways descended from this fortress into the temple so that, should rebellion flare among the Jews, six thousand armed legionaries might be emptied within the courts in a space of moments. Roman guards, posted upon the galleries, kept unceasing vigilance over all that passed below, watching upon the Jews with curiosity, beholding the sacred rites of their Passover with derision and contempt.

A vast company had entered the gates of Jerusalem with the pilgrims of Nazareth, yet now the families drew apart, one from the other, going forth to lodgings with friends and kinsmen, searching out seemly places for encampment upon the slopes and hilltops. Yet Cleophas, Zebedee, and Joseph remained together, their wives and children beside them, the lads turning to Joseph as they went forward into the city, eager to hear what words he would utter concerning its marvels.

They gazed with wonder upon the multitude of Jews thronging the streets, at the great houses of the ruling families of Jerusalem . . . Jewish nobles, elders, and priests who, for paying court to their Roman conquerors, had been rewarded with position and riches. They dwelt in the fashion of those in Rome, mingled with Roman officials and nobles, sent their sons across the Great Sea to be schooled in Roman cities. And they were despised in the eyes of all honorable men, seeing that they had turned their faces from the oppression of their own people, the dishonoring of their own God.

From the ancient streets of Jerusalem rose many palaces, among them the aged palace of Jewish kings, the magnificent and beautiful palace built by the dead Herod, the palaces of the High Priest and his family behind massive walls and brazen gates. It was said that the gardens of the High Priest were exquisite beyond the telling, filled with numberless flowers and majestic trees nourished with the blood of the temple sacrifices.

Drawn by their own wonder and curiosity, large numbers of foreigners entered Jerusalem at the season of the Passover, many of them Romans. One beheld the men, erect and remote, clad in the sandals and togas of their own land, passing arrogantly through the streets, attended by those who served them. Roman women, white of flesh, dark of hair, at times exceedingly beautiful, were borne in rich litters by slaves handsomely garbed. Yet, despite their own curiosity, the Jews would not look upon their conquerors, but turned their faces from them, and from the sight of the numberless legionaries passing in rigid formation among them. The eyes of these soldiers gazed beyond; their faces were stern and unyielding as they marched through the city, magnificently trained, magnificently disciplined, magnificently hated by the sons of Abraham who, for the sake of their own lives, fell back that they might pass.

For a little time, those of Nazareth entered the streets of the sellers, the great Jerusalem market where craftsmen labored and vendors shouted amid all manner of wares. Then, seeing that the evening was soon to be upon them, they went forth to seek a place of encampment.

"In the season of the Passover," Joseph said, "all things are made to appear cleanly and new. Behold, even the sepulchers are whited as though, beholding them thus, the pilgrims will cease to remember that death and rotted bones lie within."

That night they slumbered, like many others of the pilgrimage, upon one of the slopes a little way beyond. Supper fires sprang up in the swift Judean darkness, the first star glittered in the western sky above the waters of the Great Sea. And, after a time, there rose the paschal moon, casting a white, unearthly radiance upon the temple of the Lord where certain watchmen intoned from the walls, "Is all well?" and others answered, "All is well."

Tents had been raised for the women and the younger children of Cleophas, James and the little Joses and the newborn daughter. But Joseph and Cleophas and Zebedee slumbered near the fires, wrapped in their woolen cloaks, and the lads also . . . Simon and Jude, the sons of Cleophas, James and John, the sons of Zebedee, and the young Jesus.

Mary and Salome and Mary Cleophas cleared away what remained of the evening bread, speaking together in pleasing companionship of such things as concern the hearts of women. Then, perceiving the lateness of the hour, they spread forth their bed mats, quenched the flame of the lamp, and fell into slumber.

With the first gleaming shafts of morning, the rams' horns were sounded and priests, clad in the fairest of their vestments, moved in a long and unwavering line to the first rituals of the day. Joseph went forth, with Cleophas and Zebedee, to the buying of a lamb of sacrifice, the lads beside him. According to the holy law, the animal must bear neither spot nor blemish. It could be offered upon the altar of God only after the priests had declared it undefiled, and they rejected all save those purchased in the temple market at a price set by the High Priest. Since this was beyond the purse of a humble pilgrim, it fell to the three men of Galilee to share the cost and divide the flesh of a single animal.

Afterward, Mary's son told her how it was that they had purchased a warrant for a small lamb which they would receive at a certain gate, and at a certain hour of sacrifice. He and the other lads had lingered in the Court of Gentiles, desiring to behold all that passed, had made their way through the throngs and entered Solomon's Porch, the cloistered area to the east where teachers and their pupils gathered, speaking together of the meaning of the law and the coming of the promised Messiah. Nor were the Galilean youths thrust aside, but instead shown deference, seeing that they sought both righteousness and learning.

They had beheld certain men of the law whom Joseph called Sadducees and Pharisees, and he had told them much concerning these. The Sadducees, he said, were learned and wealthy Jews who had befriended the Romans and taken unto themselves many Roman ways. Being world-minded, they were derisive of prophecies concerning a Messiah, of talk which dealt with life after death. The Pharisees were other Jews who, as interpreters of the law, honored their own piety and scorned the humble, the untaught. In truth, it was no uncommon thing to behold them praying on the corners of the streets, or in some unhidden portion of the synagogue, that all might see and proclaim their devotion to the Lord.

Afterward, the lad Jesus had perceived, against the temple wall, a row of thirteen heavy chests with openings for receiving money offered as tithes or gifts, and to these came worshipers beyond the counting. There were some who dropped a few coins softly and quietly, for their hearts were humble, and their purses poor. There were others, desiring to have their righteousness known abroad, who cast in a multitude of coins, with clamor pleasing to their ears. A certain Sadducee did not even touch the coins he bestowed upon the temple, but instead signed his slave to come forward and empty into one of the chests a bag of shekels borne from his house.

And now Mary perceived that the face of her son had grown grave and reflective.

"There was one among them, my mother . . ." he said, "a widow with her little children about her, poorly clad and thin, as though she hungered. One would not believe her able to spare as much as a mite, even though it is the smallest of coins. And, in truth, it was all she possessed, yet she gave it gladly, out of her love and goodness. And it came to me that her deed is greater in the eyes of our Lord than the deeds of all those, together, who give tithes of neither hardship nor want."

Mary stroked his hair, putting it back from his flushed and sweating brow as he sat beside her, one brown arm outflung across his knee. Hearing his words, she knew a sense of sadness that was at once pride and regret. And she said in her heart: With this day, I have ceased to be his teacher. Henceforth, it is I who will listen, and he who will utter the syllables of righteousness and wisdom.

XIII.

IMPRINTED UPON THE WARRANT HELD BY ZEBEDEE WAS THE precise time at which the paschal lamb would be delivered at the gate beyond the altar of sacrifice. Thus, a little past the hour of noonday, the families set forth from the encampment on the hillside, made fair and clean, clad in the most seemly of their simple garments, that they might be pleasing in the house of the Lord.

The outer court of the temple, burning in the heat of the sun, thronged by a multitude of pilgrims, appeared both clamorous and disordered. Indeed, it was filled with the voices and striving of the multitude, the passing to and fro of temple priests, the hastening forth of guards and porters, the cries of the money-changers, the gathering of the curious around the tables of scribes who, with goose-quill pens, wrote prayers for the buying. On every side, voices were lifted in talk, laughter, dissension, countless languages and manners of speech. One heard the cooing of doves in the temple market, the distant lowing of the cattle and bleating of the sheep awaiting the slaughter, the clamor of money cast into the chests along the walls, the weeping of children divided from their mothers in the throng. And over all, there rose the stench of smoke and scorching fat, mingled with the heavy sweetness of incense.

Amid the chanting of mellow voices and the sound of

trumpets stood the Levites, an order of priests descended from Aaron, brother of Moses. Ranged upon the marble steps, they plucked the strings of scrolled harps as they offered before the Lord the psalms appointed for this day. When each psalm had come to its end, the trumpets were sounded as a signal for prayers, and afterward another psalm begun. It was a sight strange and beautiful, long to be remembered: the white-clad priests chanting their plaintive orisons before a gate which gleamed with gold.

Mary, with Salome and Mary Cleophas, passed within the Court of Women from which they would behold the sacrifice. Their husbands, together with their sons, went forth to a certain gate for the claiming of the lamb. Beyond this gate, thousands of sheep milled about, bleating sorrowfully out of their fear, their wretchedness in the burning sun, the blown dust. Joseph lifted up the lamb given to his hands and it lay upon his shoulders, small and white and perfect, limp by reason of its own terror. It was piteously still, uttering no sound, making no resistance, only awaiting what would come. Whereupon Joseph, followed by the others, went forth to the Court of Israel, ascending the same steps climbed by unending lines of priests bearing holy vessels and incense.

As he entered, the silver trumpets were lifted and sounded three times. Those from Galilee placed their hands upon the little lamb, as a sign that he was dying for the remission of their sins thus laid upon him, and cast him down so that the length of his body lay between north and south. Swiftly, his throat was severed, his blood caught in a golden vessel by one of the priestly attendants, and passed down the line of still other priests until it was given to him who stood nearest the holy fire, and who cast it upon the base of the altar.

The slaughtered lamb was then hung up and dressed, the fat being burned as an offering before the Lord, the refuse being washed away by the water drawn in great pails from the cistern beneath. Then, taking up the flesh and pelt which remained, Joseph and those of his small company turned again to the outer court to await the coming forth of the women.

Even as they came together, they hastened to the hillside of their encampment, that they might make ready the feast of the Passover. Earlier, a cooking trench had been prepared and laid with brushwood. And when, at length, the savor of browning meat rose from the coals, Mary Cleophas spoke to the watching lads in lively consolation, saying that only a little time would be required for the roasting of flesh so young and tender. She and her sisters set their hands to the baking of the unleavened bread, the small and flat wafers sacred to the day. They set forth fruit and vegetables and wine and, according to the custom, wild herbs gathered in the hills, bay and thyme and basil and the bitter, pungent marjoram.

With every family of pilgrims, whether poor or untaught, rich or learned, it was the same. The feast began with the going down of the sun when, according to the ancient command, all who were of the House of Israel gathered to keep the Passover and give thanks to God for this holy night.

"Blessed Thou art, O Lord, who has chosen us above all peoples, and has exalted us above all tongues, and has hallowed us with Thy commandments. And Thou has given us, Lord, with love, Sabbaths for rest, seasons for gladness, holidays and times for rejoicing, this day of the Festival of the Unleavened Bread . . . an assembly day of holiness. . . ."

And of the unleavened bread sacred to this feast, they declared together, "This is the poor bread which our fathers ate in the land of Egypt. Let anyone who is hungry come and eat. Let anyone who is needy come and make the Passover. . . ."

The bread, in small flat wafers, an ancient memorial of the release from bondage, was dipped in a sauce of wine and nuts and fruit. A cup of wine was blessed and passed and salt water tasted in memory of the bitter tears shed in the years when their people were the slaves of Pharaoh. And the youngest son asked, "How is this night different from other nights?" He was answered with the story of the going forth from Egypt, in the words by which the Lord had commanded, "And this day shall be to you a memorial, and you shall keep it a feast to the Lord throughout all generations. . . ."

And it was declared, "Therefore it is our duty to thank Him . . . who brought us forth from slavery to freedom, from sorrow to joy, from mourning to festive day, and from darkness to a great light."

And all of the company lifted their voices in the singing of certain psalms.

"May the name of the Lord be blessed from now unto all eternity.

"From the dawning place of the sun to its setting place . . . praised be the name of the Lord.

"Exalted above all nations is the Lord, over all the heavens in his glory.

"Who is like unto the Lord, our God, who dwells on high and sees what is below, in the heavens and in the earth?

"He lifts up the poor from the dust. . . .

"He raises the lowly, to seat them with the nobles of his people. . . .

"He brings the uprooted to a new home, and the mothers of children rejoice. Praise ye the name of the Lord."

The second cup of wine was taken and the meal of the Passover eaten, divided among the families of Joseph, Cleophas, and Zebedee, seeing that as many as twenty might eat from a single lamb. The third and fourth cups were filled and blessed, the fourth being the "cup of benediction" passed during the singing of the last psalm, the closing of the feast said to be "as delectable as the olive."

"Not unto us, O Lord, but to thy name give glory.

"The Lord has been mindful of us. He will bless the house of Israel.

"May the Lord add to you and to your children.

"We shall praise Him henceforth and forever."

Long before the hour of midnight, the flesh of every lamb of sacrifice had been eaten, every cup of benediction drained, every voice lifted in the hymn of praise: *"O, give thanks unto the Lord . . . for He is good . . . and His mercy endureth forever."* Now there rose above the quiet hills a paschal moon of such radiance that the embers of a thousand supper fires became as ashes in its light. Wearied by the festive day, those of the pilgrimage had fallen into slumber and the silence of peace lay upon the countryside. Even in the streets of Jerusalem, there was no sound save the echoing tread of those who stood against the evils of the night: the watchmen at the gates, the guards of the temple, the lonely sentries along the towering walls of the Roman fortress.

In the dimness of the tent of women, Mary lay quietly. Pale shafts of moonlight, slanting through the doorway, fell upon the strong young figure of Mary Cleophas, the pleasant face of Salome, merry even in slumber. Their slow and even breaths, mingled with those of the young children, revealed the measure of their serenity. The men had long since ceased speaking together and turned to the comforting oblivion of their cloaks. The sons of Zebedee slumbered side by side, the arm of the sturdy James laid protectingly across the shoulders of the slighter John. The elder sons of Cleophas had lain down together also but Simon, being both selfish and arrogant, had seized the better cloak and the place nearer the warmth of the coals, without regard for Jude. And Mary perceived that her own son had not slept, but lay with wide-open eyes, gazing into

114

the radiance of the sweet spring night, intent upon such thoughts as came to him through the dreaming silences.

She yearned to go forth to him and yet would not, seeing that he was no longer a child, but a son of the law, apart from the tents of the women. And a sense of the fleetness of time assailed her desolately. More than a length of twelve years had passed the night when she had spoken with a messenger of the Lord. In truth, all that passed in that hour had become both remote and unreal, in the manner of a dream only half recalled. She and Joseph had shielded their secret with such prudence that should the Magi themselves enter Nazareth declaring: "Behold the Christ . . ." the villagers would be filled with merriment. Then, in scorn as well as mirth, they would demand, "Is this not the son of Joseph the carpenter, and of his wife Mary, daughter of Joachim and Anne? Is this not their son, born in the time of the census?" And they would shrug the matter from them with some light, unburdened word: "These strangers have been tasting new wine. . . ."

With austerity, she had put her son's destiny from her lips and thoughts, closing it within the temple of her heart, awaiting the will of the Lord. At times, she ceased to remember, for the space of a moment, that he was not a humble peasant child. Yet this day, beholding the sacrifice, she had been seized by an unforgotten terror, recalling the words of the prophecy: ". . . *he shall be led as a lamb to the slaughter* . . ." so that she was rendered sleepless by her own disquiet.

Yet with the lad Jesus, it was otherwise. Awake, in the watches of the night, he knew no uneasiness, but only the vast sense of wonder and reverence which came to every worthy son of Israel on the night of his first Passover.

Now surely the words of the scriptures returned to him, out of the hallowed past. "And the Lord spake unto Moses saying . . . And it shall come to pass, when your children say unto you: What mean ye by this service? . . . that ye shall say it is a night to be kept in thanksgiving to the Lord for bringing ye out of Egypt. This is that night of the Lord to be observed by all the children of Israel in all generations. . . ."

Yes, truly, the wonder of this night, holy beyond all others, possessed the heart of her son, even as his spirit was lifted up in love for his heavenly Father. And she perceived that, as he lay gazing into the unending reaches of the firmament, upon the unalterable stars and the ancient radiance of the moon, he would have cried out, even as the psalmist, "When I behold the heavens, the work of Thy hands, what is man . . . that Thou art mindful of him?"

Yet, with morning, the splendor of the moment had departed, even as the still glory of the night. In the dust and clamor and burning heat of day, those of Galilee set forth from Jerusalem, concerned once again with all that awaited them . . . the tilling of their fields, the pruning of their trees and vineyards, the tending of their flocks, the striving against flood and storm and locusts and the terrors of drought, the unceasing toil that was like a heavy yoke upon them, seeing that any gains thereof must be rendered up to Rome or borne in tithes to the temple.

Yearning to enter the doors of their own houses, even as they had yearned to go forth upon the journey, the families of Nazareth took up their goods, cast loads upon their animals and upon their own shoulders, and moved northward from the city gates in a great exodus astonishing to the Romans who beheld it.

By reason of the unsparing heat and choking dust, the striving and milling multitude, it was not possible for family gatherings to remain undivided. Each among them went forth as he was able until, coming upon a chosen landmark at the end of the day's journey, he separated himself from the throng and awaited brethren or neighbors. Thus neither Mary nor Joseph was troubled when, as they traveled, they discerned no sight of Jesus among those who pressed about them. From her place on the donkey, Mary was able to gaze a distance beyond, and shielding her eyes with her hand, she sought often for some glimpse of her son's lithe young figure, his high head and dark, rumpled hair. Yet he was not to be found among the streaming pilgrims, nor were Simon and Jude.

At the going down of the sun, she and Joseph halted near a certain well of Beeroth to await the families from their own village. And, with the coming of the first of these, fires were kindled, bed mats cast down, the evening bread set forth. More and yet more of the Nazareth neighbors arrived. Children were sought and claimed, brethren reunited, tidings of the journey passed from mouth to mouth. After a time, Simon and Jude appeared, stumbling with weariness, lamenting their hunger, and were given bread by the diligent Mary Cleophas.

Not until every other lad had entered the encampment and been counted did Mary fear for her son. Even then she sought to still her panic with reasoning words spoken, not to Joseph, but to herself: He is with Zebedee and Salome, even as John has come to me. In but a little time they will be among us, and Jesus also. . . .

Yet when the stalwart brown figure of the Galilean fisherman strode out of the darkness into the wavering radiance of the supper fires, only his wife walked beside him. The lad Jesus was not with them, nor had they encountered him upon the way.

Assailed by strengthening fear, Mary hastened from fire to fire, from tent to tent, beseeching those before her, saying, "In what place did you last look upon my son?" . . . saying, "It was my thought . . . surely he abides with you. . . ." Asking, "Are you certain he has not fallen into slumber with the lads from Capernaum?"

Yet neither her own searching nor that of Joseph revealed a single word concerning him. Those of Nazareth, sharing their alarm, rose up from their rest, their evening bread, and took up the search, asking throughout the encampment for word of the beloved lad. Yet none recalled that they had looked upon him since the dawn of that day. Salome had believed him with his parents . . . Mary Cleophas had thought the same.

It was late at night, with the waning moon long risen, when Joseph and Mary saddled the donkey, gathered up their goods, and turned back to the holy city, seeking their son. One of the Galilean pilgrims, a kindly woman from Nain, ran to the side of the animal and sought to bring comfort to Mary, seizing her hand.

"Seek out my sister Jerusha, widow of Enoch, for she is a godly woman and will give you both shelter and bread. . . ."

Throughout the night they journeyed, hastened by terror, unmindful of the weariness, the steep ascents, the stirred dust, the chill of darkness. The way was bordered by encampments of pilgrims where watch fires fell into ashes and families slumbered undisturbed. At times they came upon small groups who were traveling through the night and sought among them for some word of the lad, but he was known to none. They approached the gates of Jerusalem in the first pale radiance of dawn, while the watchmen were quenching their lanterns, the fortress echoed with the bugles which sounded for the changing of the guard, the cocks were crowing beyond the hills, the lepers and beggars and cripples were crawling to their posts near the highroad.

The house of the widow Jerusha was easily found, and her hands held forth to them with unrestrained generosity. Yet Mary could neither slumber nor partake of morning bread, and when she had bathed and garbed herself in seemly garments, besought Joseph to go forth again into the streets of the city. And she perceived that his anxiety was no less than her own, that his face was filled with wretchedness, his eyes clouded and fearful.

Throughout the day, they took neither food nor sleep, but hastened from street to street, searching, questioning, imploring all they met for some tidings of Jesus. Oh, my son, thought Mary, in despair, where are you in this unhappy hour? Who holds you from your family, if indeed you yet live and have not perished?

And when the sun had descended into the Great Sea and the swift purple twilight had darkened the hills of Moab toward the east, she turned back again with Joseph beside her, past speech in her utter weariness.

The elderly Jerusha, widow of a wealthy merchant, dwelt in a spacious house sheltered from the burning of the sun by tall green trees. Her servantwoman had laid a clean cloth for the two from Nazareth, and spread upon it a goodly meal, fruit and meat and new bread set forth in the light of a burnished lamp. In truth, they had no wish for food, yet for the sake of courtesy, they ate of it and afterward were comforted somewhat.

"This night, beloved, you must rest," said Joseph, for he perceived that Mary's eyes were dazed with weariness, her face white and stricken. And, fearing for her, he sought to solace her with words which he himself was unable to believe. "It may be that, even now, he has reached our brethren at Beeroth."

"Nay, for Cleophas promised the sending of some message, should this come to pass."

"With morning, such word may be brought to us," he said, and spoke with heartiness, even though he was certain that it would not be so. Then, after a little time, he turned to her again, made shamed and wondering by his own doubt. "No harm will befall a lad who is chosen of the Lord. . . ."

"Even so," she said presently and, finding peace in the

119

thought, allowed him to lead her to the bed which had been prepared for her in an upper room.

Long after Joseph slumbered, she lay staring out over the quiet hills in lonely wretchedness, knowing there were men who sold into slavery youths encountered alone, and without the protection of companions or kinsmen. And she cried out before the Lord, "Oh, how is it that I, Your unworthy handmaiden, have cared so poorly for the son You entrusted to my hands?"

Yet after a time she slept, only to rouse with the first crowing of the cocks, to set forth with Joseph beside her. And so it was until the third day when, as they approached the gleaming temple of God, Mary cried out, "The teachers of the Porch ... only think how it was that he hastened forth to them, yearning to hear all that passed among them! In truth, it may be that they have some word of him. . . ."

And thus their steps quickened as they entered the Court of Gentiles and hastened eastward to the Porch of Solomon, where sat certain doctors of the law, majestic bearded men, richly clad and adorned, with their scholars before them.

Mary and Joseph halted for a moment, reluctant to enter a gathering plainly intent upon listening to the words of a great teacher. Then, drawing nearer, and gazing over the heads of the reclining doctors, they perceived that the teacher was a lad in a fair tunic, wrought for him by the loving hands of his mother.

"*My son!*" The words were wrenched from Mary's lips, even as her astonishment, her anguish of heart. Hastening to him, she fell upon her knees and embraced him, her uplifted face a prayer of wordless thanksgiving. Those of the Porch, out of their respect for all who were mothers, waited in silence, and Joseph also. Whereupon they heard her voice lifted in quiet **rebuke.**

"Son, wherefore have you dealt with us in this manner? Behold, we have sought you sorrowing. . . ."

For a moment he gazed upon their faces, and when at length he answered, his young voice was filled with astonishment.

"How is it that you have sought me?" he asked, in innocent wonder. "Did you not know I must be about my Father's business?"

Mary gazed at him, making no answer, bewildered beyond utterance. Surely, she said to herself, it is too soon for the voice of the Lord to stir within him, rousing him to the nature of his destiny. . . .

Then the doctors of the law rose up, praising the wisdom of the lad, showing him honor and uncommon respect. Yet when Mary and Joseph set forth from the temple, he walked between them, holding their hands, and was no longer a teacher of the learned, but a youthful son of Galilee rejoicing in the sight of his parents, subject to them. Even so, Mary suffered great heaviness of spirit. In but a little time . . . she thought desolately. Yet she uttered no word of that which troubled her, keeping it closed within her heart.

XIV.

At times it seemed, in mary's weariness, that the years were a caravan of donkeys all alike, loaded with heavy and unchanging burdens to the last measure of their strength, yet moving swiftly and in disorder, as though scourged forward by the lash of a relentless driver. One after another, they passed and were gone, leaving, by reason of their haste, little imprint upon the dust of Nazareth.

Yet the lad Jesus grew taller and stronger and more comely with their passing and, unlike other sons of the village, sought to spare his mother some of the striving of a woman's life. From the earliest years of his boyhood, he had gazed with pitying and reflective eyes upon the woman of Nazareth, knowing with what unending drudgery they toiled in the fields and gardens, gathered in the harvests, bore the heavy water jars, kept the house, labored with flax and wool, with spinning and weaving and dyeing, the washing and seaming of garments, the cooking and storing of the food, the milking and feeding of the animals, the bearing and tending and teaching of their children. He perceived how it was that daughters of Galilee, as young as their thirteenth year, toiled beside their husbands even when heavy with an unborn child, knowing less of tenderness than the donkey or the ox.

Thus he went forth with Mary to many of her appointed tasks, lifting from her frail shoulders countless burdens of

122

garden, field, and vineyard. Yet there was no day wherein he did not labor beside Joseph in the carpenter shop, amid the cherished tools, the sweet-smelling wood, the shapes of wheels and yokes and plows and chests. Dealing with the tasks of the household, Mary would hear his voice lifted in youthful questioning, and the deep tones of Joseph answering that which he had asked.

"Nay, my son. For a house which shall stand against the floods of spring, a man must dig down and down, below all earth, to the region of rock . . . at times, as much as the height of a tall tree. Such a foundation, no storm may destroy, seeing that it is built, not upon the unfixed sand and clods, but upon a rock."

And she perceived with what regard the lad heard the words of the beloved carpenter, knowing him both wise and skilled.

In the season of planting, the youth went forth with them to the fields. More than once he had held small seeds within his hand and spoken to Mary of the miracle of growth by which they would become broad plants bearing food . . . even the mustard seed which, though smaller than all others, might grow as high as the head of a camel. Along Lake Galilee, John had told him, one beheld mustard plants of such strength and numbers that rock pigeons roosted in their branches.

In the manner of all Galilean peasants, Joseph and Cleophas sowed the seed of their harvests by hand and, even as they toiled, crows and ravens descended from the skies and perched boldly in the branches thereabout, awaiting their departure. Then Jesus and the sons of Cleophas hastened to the fields, running and shouting and brandishing staves, that the intruders might be driven forth.

The fields of Galilee were bordered and divided by footpaths with the hardness of stone, having been trodden for uncounted years by all generations. At times the grains cast forth by the sower would fall upon these paths and thus become visible to the waiting birds, so that great flocks fluttered down, with raucous cries, to eat of it.

In places, the earth was but a thin layer of soil over lengths of rock which, under the burning rays of the sun, grew as hot as a kettle amid the flames. Seed which fell upon such soil sprang up quickly in the heat, yet being unable to sprout through the unyielding rock, died rootless and spent.

Throughout the fields grew clumps of thornweed which many knew as thistles, and should any grains fall among these, they would be choked and killed, for the thistles grew faster and more abundantly than either barley or wheat.

It was not often that a man took up a handful of wheat without darnel seeds. These poisonous weeds, known as tares, grew up with such a likeness to the grain that it was not possible to discern one from the other until the heads had taken form. Then the difference was known to all, for a tare possessed a head of small dark grains, while the head of the wheat was entirely golden. Also, the heads of the wheat were bent when the grain was ripened, but the heads of the tares stood high.

"Behold, my son," said Mary, "the plants which God has blessed bow their heads before him . . . but the tares, being evil, have no portion in humility."

From moon to moon, they watched upon their fields with tender anxiety, hoping they would bring forth many ears of wheat and few of darnel, yet a multitude of the weeds came forth.

"Only let me enter into the fields and pull out the tares by their roots," said the lad.

But Joseph shook his head.

"Should you do this thing, then truly, you would trample and ruin the harvest, my son . . . or, through error, uproot as many stalks of wheat as tares, seeing that they are not unlike. Nay, let us await the harvest, that they may be gathered separately."

124

And so, at the season of the ingathering, the dark-headed tares were plucked, bundled into sheaves, and burned. Then the wheat, ripened and sound, was harvested and stored against the time of need.

Since neither brushwood nor stone nor any other fence divided the fields, travelers often passed down the footpaths in the season of ripened grain, that they might gather kernels of wheat or barley. For, according to the law of Israel, any who journeyed through the land might eat from whatever field he should pass, should he have no other means of food. Thus it was no uncommon thing for the young Jesus to behold strangers halting beside a wheat field, that they might gather the grain, rub away the chaff, and eat the corns which, even though uncooked, were flavorsome to a hungry man.

In the season of harvest, those who labored in the fields went forth in the first reddened light of dawn, and returned only with the going down of the sun. Sheaves, cut with sickles and tied up with lengths of the slender wheat stalk, were cast aside to be loaded within a donkey cart with creaking wooden wheels, driven by one of the lads. It was the custom for reapers to be followed by the village poor, seeing that these were bidden to glean for themselves whatever grain had fallen. And, indeed, it was according to the holy law that this was done, for the words of the commands were known to all.

"When thou cuttest down thy harvest in thy field . . . and hast forgot a sheaf in the field . . . thou shalt not go forth again to fetch it. It shall be for the stranger . . . for the fatherless and the widow . . . that the Lord, thy God, may bless thee in all the work of thy hands."

And it was likewise a portion of the holy law that the oxen should labor unmuzzled, that they might be allowed to eat of the grain as they toiled, this being a reward to them.

The harvested grain was borne to the threshing floor, a hard and barren portion of field, where the sheaves of each family were laid in their own place. This being accomplished, the ox drew over the grain a heavy wooden sledge set with bits of flint and iron. These, together with the hoofs of the animal, divided the grain from the straw, and that the sledge might be given weight, the lads rode upon it, a light and merry task.

Afterward, the grain was divided from the chaff by wooden forks known as winnowing fans. With these, the women cast the threshed grain into the wind of God which blew from the Great Sea, and which bore the chaff hence, even as the wheat fell back to earth. Then, having gathered it up, the women lifted from it whatever stones were among the grain and bore it homeward, that it might be stored against the season of winter.

Each night, from the time of ripening until the harvest was gathered in and divided among those who had labored to bring it forth, certain of the lads watched over the fields, guarding them from thieves in the hours of darkness.

The season of harvest was one of village merriment, despite the long hours of unceasing toil in the heat of the sun. With midday, those who labored paused to take food in the consoling shade of a bough, roasting sheaves of wheat over a brushwood fire for their bread, slaking their thirst with a cooling drink from one of the clay jars. At times, the widows and orphans and sojourners who gleaned in their midst were bidden to the meal also, and the day was as festive as that of an espousal, or the Shearing of a Son.

In a later season, families went forth in the same manner to the ingathering of the grapes, these being plucked and heaped upon baskets or borne to the rooftops, that they might be made into vinegar and wine, or spread forth to dry in the sun. In late November, the olives were beaten from the trees by the men and youths, gathered up by the women and girls, pressed into oil for lamps and cooking and soapmaking, used as butter and medicine.

No year was like any year before it. One brought a drought when the rains ceased and the dust blew in from the desert, when men gazed with despair upon ruined harvests, animals pawed at dry troughs and empty water holes, women feared to look within the well, lest they discover it empty. There were rains which became floods, ripping forth rocks and trees and hillsides, drowning many of the flocks, even the cubs of the wilds, destroying the seeds of fields and gardens. And in the season of ripening there were, in certain years, great hailstones which shattered the corn, hurled unripe olives to the earth, severed the young grapes from the vine. In yet other years, locusts descended upon the land, so that the sky was darkened as by a storm, and every branch and stalk stripped of its verdure.

When at length Jesus had entered his fourteenth year, the burdens which weighed upon the family were increased and made yet more oppressive. For Cleophas died, having been stricken with the trembling fever which sometimes rose from the slime-strewn marshes in the heat of summer. And, according to the custom, his widow and children were left to the care of the nearest kinsman. In truth, the sons of Cleophas had been taught the ways of labor, and toiled in field and vineyard as diligently as their father before them, yet seeing that they were only striplings, it fell to Joseph to spare the family from want.

They did not dwell together, Mary Cleophas remaining within her own house, but the lads James and Jude came to serve in the shop of Joseph, that the skills of carpentry might be made known to them. Simon kept to the labor of his father, that of tilling the soil, for he was solitary and obstinate, and had no liking for instruction.

The families went forth together, as was seemly, on the

morning of every Sabbath, that they might worship in the village synagogue, Joseph and the young Jesus leading the way. The others followed after, Mary in a soft tunic and embroidered girdle, her dark parted hair combed smoothly away from her delicate brow, a veil cast modestly over her head, falling upon her small shoulders. The figure of Mary Cleophas was still sturdy and youthful, though her hands, scarred by unceasing toil, were the hands of age, and her comely face had become thin and desolate before the measure of her sorrow. The children of her house now numbered six, for after Simon and James and Joses and Jude, two daughters had been born to her.

Joseph, tall and straight and brown, would appear all the days of his life as a man well-favored, of dignity and virtue. Yet there was a vast weariness upon him, and an unrelieved sadness. For he was burdened by the sufferings of his people, their want, their oppressions, their despair. Tilling the soil in the fields of the mountains was not easily done, even when the seasons were fair, the sun benevolent. And when, at length, the striving against drought and heat and storm were ended, tithes and taxes seized from every man the meager gains brought into being by the painful sweat of his brow and the unsparing labor of his hands.

On a certain afternoon in late summer, when drought assailed the countryside and the heat was not unlike the flame of a grass fire, Joseph was stricken with an illness swift and terrifying. His strength departed from him so suddenly that his square fell from his hand, clattering upon the floor and, turning quickly, the young Jesus perceived that he was white and sweating, unable to stand against the pain upon him.

Mary, hearing the youth cry out, came quickly from her labors within the house and, together, they knelt beside the stricken man, seeking to bring him aid. They were filled with

128

terror, perceiving that he fought, hoarse and gasping, for the strength to breathe, that some unnamed agony had seized upon his breast beneath his clutching fingers. And Mary's voice, when she spoke, was lonely and afraid.

"Beloved . . . what is it?"

Even in his agony, he knew what distress was upon her, and sought to speak in consolation.

"Nay . . . nay . . . have no fear. It will pass . . . as it has done before. . . ."

And only then was it revealed to her that he had suffered more than once in the same fashion.

The lad, shaken and fearful, had cast himself down and was striving to cleanse the dripping sweat from the brow of him whom he called father.

"I will go forth and bring cooling water. . . ."

But the worn and gentle hand of Joseph stayed him.

"Nay, my son. Do not depart from me. . . ."

And though he uttered no word further, Mary perceived what was passing in his mind. Stay beside me, my son, for there is little enough time that we may spend together. Stay beside me, my child, my dear one, whose destiny I shall not live to behold. . . .

And her heart was quickened by terror, so that she put both her arms about her husband, as though she would shield him from all evil, and held him against her breast. And now, turning his face to her, he sought to ease her disquiet.

"Behold, the pain has gone from me . . . as before. . . ."

Yet even while they spoke together, each striving to console the other, it was known to them that this illness was not a passing thing, to be forgotten, to afflict him no more. Tears stood in Mary's eyes as she gazed upon him.

"I would not have you suffer pain, beloved."

He reached forth and laid his hand over her own.

"My saintly one . . . in whom I have been blessed by the Lord. . . ."

It was as if the stream of their love flowed, quickened, between them, living and imperishable. And afterward, it came to her that despite all other words which passed between them from that hour, these were the words of their farewell.

XV.

THE PALE BLOSSOMS OF THE ALMOND TREE HAD FALLEN MANY
times upon the tomb where Joseph lay, brought to his death
in the richest years of his life by toil and striving. For a length
of fifteen years, Mary had dwelt in the small house with her
son, and the tools of carpenter and joiner had been taken up by
his strong brown hands. Being the eldest son, he had become
head of the family in Nazareth, and the sons of Cleophas looked
to him with seemly regard for his years and wisdom, even
though they were but little younger.

He had grown tall and brown and comely, as straight as a
cypress, filled with quiet thoughtfulness, gentle speech, and
ready laughter. By those of the village he was loved beyond
all others of his years, and the elderly women gazed upon him
with shrewd, contemplative eyes, thinking of unwed daughters
and nieces. Yet, even though he was nearing the thirtieth year
of his life, he had uttered no word of marriage, nor looked
upon any daughter of the village, however fair, with more than
neighborly affection. He labored within the doors of the shop,
set his hand to the sowing and reaping and garnering, went
forth with merry heart to the feasts and espousals and mar-
riages, led his brethren up to the Passover in the season of the
barley, took his own place in the synagogue, that he might keep
the Sabbath before the Lord. Like Joseph before him, he often
lingered by a kindled lamp until the late hours of the night,

searching the scriptures, studying the scrolls of the law. And those of Nazareth, perceiving the righteousness of his heart, declared among themselves, "Truly, this man is loved of the Lord. . . ."

The days were as swift as a weaver's shuttle, and brought forth, in the same manner, the timeless pattern of uncounted generations, fixed and familiar, not to be changed. Then, suddenly, with the tumult of a storm there strode, out of the obscurity of years, the son of Zacharias and Elizabeth.

It was after the ingathering of the olives, near the pouring forth of the winter rains, when those of Nazareth first spoke of this man, having been given word of him by passing caravans, by merchants and craftsmen lately returned from markets beyond the village, from all who halted at the well. And indeed, his name was on the lips of hundreds who had never looked upon his face, for his words were the rumor of every bazaar, the discourse of the highroads.

He was, they declared, a holy man of the Lord, even as the prophets of their fathers, seeking no portion in the realms of the flesh, desiring the realms of the spirit only. And, in truth, he bore but meager likeness to other men, save only to the Essenes, whom few had looked upon.

Brought to manhood in the austerity of their life and teachings, he was a creature of the wilderness. His hair was both long and shaggy, it being a matter of vainglory in his eyes to have it sheared, or made smooth by ointments. He was clad in a coarse garment of camel's-hair cloth girded with a leathern belt, for thus did those of the brotherhood garb themselves, with fabric woven upon their own looms, leather shaped by their own hands.

Though still in the thirtieth year of his life, he was as gaunt as one wasted by age, from fasting and labor in the heat of the sun. His flesh was as brown as the rocks of the desert, his dark eyes aflame with a holy light: a man of singular strength

132

and will, walking in righteousness, fearful of none save the Lord.

From out of the wilderness of the Dead Sea he came, from the desert solitudes, from the nights of stars, days among the stones and silences, the undefinable realms of prayer and penitence, an unquenchable yearning for holiness aflame within his soul. And his voice was heard even in Jerusalem, in Hebron and Capernaum and Cana and Bethsaida, in all the cities of the coast, even in the fastness of the mountains, the deep loneliness of the valleys, along the shores of river and lake, sounding in the ears of the highborn and the lowly, the nobles of the house of Herod, the sons of lepers and beggars, crying out the words no man desires to hear, *"Repent! For you are evil in the sight of the Lord!"*

Thus he pointed a condemning finger at a sinful world, at those who had turned from the ways of the Lord into the broader paths of the ungodly . . . the Jews who received their Roman conquerors as brothers for the sake of gain . . . the publicans who robbed the purses of their own people . . . men who cast aside the wives of years for a shameless, red-lipped maid . . . High Priests who extracted such a measure of tribute as to impoverish the faithful . . . Romans who worshiped the dead emperor Augustus, building temples and altars to his name, calling him a God . . . the disorderly throngs of the arena, joyous to behold a beast devouring a living man . . . the host of the Lord divided by its own obstinacy into Sadducees and Pharisees contending against one another . . . shameless Roman theatres where the sons of pagans came forth uncovered and in their nakedness . . . legionaries who set upon the Jews without mercy, who had struck down the aged, mothers heavy with children unborn, even little ones, destroying homes and lives for tribute unpaid, a rebellious deed, a word spoken in anger . . . the rich who feasted beside flowing streams while the lowly died in the streets beyond their gardens, for want of a cup of water, a crust of bread. Awed by neither rank nor station, the son of Zacharias lifted up his voice against them, crying their evil into their own ears. Nothing could quench the holy fire which burned within his bosom. In truth, he was not unlike a blazing star streaming across a realm of fetid darkness.

It was said that all Jerusalem went forth to look upon him, likewise those of the villages, the little towns, the desert and the sown, the nobles of the house of Herod, the Jews and Romans who conspired together for the sake of riches, even legionaries who halted in their march from Jericho to hear what words came forth from the mouth of the strange prophet on the banks of the Jordan River. And he cried out before them, "Repent! For the kingdom of heaven is at hand!"

He besought them to be baptized in the waters of the stream, confessing their sins, as a symbol of their repentance, a sign of their yearning to go forth into a new existence of the spirit.

Whereupon they turned to one another asking, "Is this the Messiah?"

But he answered them nay.

"I am he of whom the prophet Isaiah spoke . . . the voice crying in the wilderness: Prepare the way of the Lord!"

And a great murmuring arose among those who listened, for the words of their ancient prophets were known to them. The prophet Malachi had declared the Lord would send, before his Messiah, one who would prepare the way for his coming. And the prophet Isaiah had commanded them to harken to "a voice crying in the wilderness: Prepare the way of the Lord!"

Thus many went forth to him who was called John, and were baptized in the waters of the Jordan, confessing their sins. And still others came forth from the holy city, and from all the province of Judea, from Jericho and Bethany and the regions of the desert.

And when he saw before him certain Pharisees and Sadducees, he turned upon them crying, "O generation of vipers! Who has warned you to flee from the wrath to come?"

For he recalled how it was that the vipers of the wilderness fled before the destroying grass fires of summer, even as the wicked flee before the judgment of the Lord.

And he hurled his wrath against them, saying they would not, as they declared, be spared destruction by being the children of Abraham, but only if they possessed the humility and righteousness of Abraham's heart.

"The axe is laid unto the root of the trees," he cried, and it was known to them that he spoke of their nation, "and every tree that has not brought forth good fruit will be hewn down and cast into the fire!"

Then there were some, humbled before his mighty words, who asked of him, "What shall we do?"

Whereupon he spoke to those of high houses, richly clothed and adorned, recalling before them the ancient command of the Jews: "What is hateful to you, do not do unto others. That is the entire law." And he said, "If you have two coats, give to him who has none. And if you have meat, do likewise."

There were also publicans who came forth to be baptized, asking, "What shall we do?"

And he said to them, "Take from men no more than is just."

Then certain soldiers of Herod were baptized by him, asking the same. Whereupon he said to them, "Do violence to no man, and be content with your wages." For it was not uncommon for the soldiers of both Herod and Caesar to enrich their own purses through bribes, robbery, and the levying of unjust tribute.

Thus, day upon day, he preached the word of the Lord, not

to the Jews alone, but to aliens and pagans also, those of Rome and of Samaria, even travelers from certain islands in the Great Sea, for a multitude was gathered about the prophet known to them as John the Baptist. Yet they murmured that surely he was the Messiah, the Christ who was to come.

But he answered them saying, "I baptize you with water, but there is one mightier than I, the latchet of whose shoes I am not worthy to unloose. He shall baptize you with the Holy Spirit and with fire. . . .

"His winnowing fan is his hand, and he will thoroughly cleanse his threshing floor, and gather the wheat into his garner, but the chaff he will burn with a fire unquenchable. . . ."

Out of the dreary waste in which he had grown to manhood, the stern and terrible wilderness of unending hills and desolate ravines and great rocks shattered by convulsive heavings of the earth, he took images known and familiar with which to enrich his teachings . . . the winnowing fan of the harvest, the chaff scattered by the wind, the vipers fleeing before destruction, dead trees hewn down for firewood in the tangled growth along the Jordan.

And his voice thundered forth the searing word *"Repent!"* Disclose the weakness of your spirit and know strength. Show forth the misery of your soul and rejoice. Empty the temple of your spirit and be filled.

And of the many baptized by him, some did not turn homeward, but lingered and became disciples in his name.

Again and again there came to Nazareth word of this strange prophet who summoned men forth to cleanse their souls in the waters of repentance, and the stream of the Jordan.

It had long been known to Mary who it was who had emerged from the solitary reaches of the wilderness, and whose way he had come to prepare. Thus, on a certain evening, she turned to her son and made the matter known to him, saying

136

simply, "He whom men call John the Baptist . . . the same is your cousin, the son of Zacharias and Elizabeth, who came into the world six moons before your birth."

They had eaten the supper bread and gone up to the roof-top together, seeking the cooling wind of dusk, with the silence of evening upon them, and the purple darkness falling across the hills beyond. Speaking gently, she lifted the fragments of the tale from the realm of her memory and laid them before him, making them orderly and whole, so that he might take them to himself, seeing that they were a portion of his own destiny.

She revealed how it was that, in yearning for the tender Elizabeth, she had made the long journey to Ain Karim and lingered there, awaiting the birth of the little John. And now, with an aching sense of irreparable loss, she recalled the quiet evenings within the small stone house, with the light of the kindled lamp gleaming upon the humble room, and upon the faces of her brethren, glorified by their own serenity.

Then, rousing from the silence which had fallen upon her, she told how it was that Zacharias had been stricken mute, in fear of the Lord, when he beheld the messenger, and doubted the words of the promise. "Fear not, Zacharias, for your prayers are heard, and your wife, Elizabeth, shall bear a son, and you shall call his name John. And you shall have joy and gladness, and many shall rejoice at his birth. For he shall be great in the sight of the Lord . . . and shall be filled with the Holy Spirit. And many of the children of Israel shall he turn unto the Lord."

She spoke of the birth of the sturdy lad, of the death of his parents, and how, dying, Zacharias had heard the voice of the Lord and obeyed it, sending his son not with those of his kindred, but into the care of the Essenes, the strange and austere brotherhood on the shores of the Dead Sea.

"And now, my son," she said, "you will ask of me: 'Where-

fore have you uttered no word of the matter before this hour?'
Then I shall say only that I waited until it seemed to me that
to speak was the will of the Lord."

He made no answer, and she gazed at him with anxiety
since, by reason of the darkness, she was not able to look upon
his face. But, after a little time, he turned to her, speaking
gently.

"Could there be any deed of yours for which I would reproach you?"

Whereupon he rose and lifted her to her feet, for the dew
was falling, and the chill of night but a little time away. And
as they descended the narrow stone steps, his strong young
arm about her lest she stumble in the dimness, he said quietly,
"It has been in my thoughts to go down to the Jordan, to him
who is called the Baptist. And surely, seeing that he is of my
brethren, this is the will of God."

XVI.

Surely she had gone to her doorway a thousand times, gazing into the street beyond, seeking his coming. The sound of a man's step in the dust, the murmur of deep and sudden laughter sent her to her feet, taut and waiting, her breath suspended, her eyes bright with yearning, then dull with shattered hope. For it was now more than forty days and nights since the going forth of her son from Nazareth, yet no word of him had come to her.

He had made ready for the journey as serenely as though he were summoned to some feast of God in the holy city, but even as she watched him, her heart was desolate with anxiety unspoken, unrevealed. The time approaches when he will go forth from his own house and return to it no more. Is this the hour . . . or shall he be spared to me a little longer? Whereupon she was shamed and reproached by her own disquiet. Truly the Lord has shown me mercy and compassion beyond that which I am worthy to receive . . . that my son was not to be called forth in the frail and unknowing years of his youth, but only in the fullness of his manhood, when he possesses the strength and wisdom to find his own path. Yes, truly, I am blessed of the Lord, even as he . . . yet what mother may see her son depart from her side without sorrow?

And she was certain in her heart that he had not thought to linger in the south. He had gone forth in the simple garb he would wear to the Lydda market, or on a day's journey of trade, bearing a few coins in his girdle, some bread and dates and cheese. She had stood in the doorway gazing after him, knowing pride in the tall, lithe figure, the broad and easy shoulders, the long strides, the lifted head. The Lord be with you, she had said, as she watched him depart, the Lord bless and keep you, the Lord make His face to shine upon you. . . . Yet the uneasiness within her would not be stilled.

None could say that she was lonely, with those of the village passing in and out to see how she fared, the youths James and Jude laboring in the carpenter shop by day, Mary Cleophas often at her side. In the years of their widowhood, the two had drawn yet nearer together, out of their loneliness and sorrow, their shared remembrances. Yet, unlike Mary Cleophas, Mary knew no sense of being utterly divided from her husband. So deep and enduring had been the love between them that it was as if he came to her with the gracious light of morning, the cool dusk of evening, in the deep watches of the night. Again and yet again, she was aware of the unforgotten tenderness which flowed upon her like a benediction, a stream of living water in the oasis of her grief. A thousand times his gentle, unforgotten words returned to her thoughts, so that she was comforted and counseled by them . . . unlike Mary Cleophas who sensed no lingering devotion in the memory of her husband, and was able to think of him only in the closed silence of the tomb.

On a certain afternoon, near the going down of the sun, they sat together in the small court behind the house, sheltered by an ancient grapevine which spread from a huge and twisted stalk beside the wall. Their hands were occupied with the embroidering of a fair tunic which was to be a wedding gift for the young Jerusha, one of the cousins in the village of Cana, a little distance to the north. And, as their needles brought into being certain leaves and blossoms and scrolls, they fell to talking of him whose name enlivened every gathering, John the Baptist.

"It has come to me," said Mary Cleophas then, "that this prophet might be our own kinsman, the son of Elizabeth, seeing that he is of the Essenes. . . ."

"Even so," answered Mary. "I have spoken to Jesus, saying the same."

"In truth," said the other quietly, "he is one whose words shall not pass away, but shall remain . . . even as the words of Jesus."

Mary's head lifted quickly.

"How is it that you speak thus of my son?"

"Always I have said in my heart that he is not destined to live out his days as a carpenter but, instead, as a rabbi in Israel." She added slowly, with an edge of bitterness, "Would that I possessed a son who might bear witness to the Lord!"

And Mary perceived it was known, even to her, that the sons of Cleophas were as blunt and unpersuasive as the clods of the earth.

Afterward, they turned again to word of the Baptist, and the manner in which he had brought upon himself the anger of Herod Antipas. For such was the talk of every traveler, the rumor of every bazaar.

It was known throughout the land that the dark and contriving ruler had long courted the favor of the Romans, even as his evil father before him. In truth, he went often to Rome, and it was while he lingered there, in the rich house of his brother Philip, that he desired Herodias, his sister-in-law.

After the way of Rome, her husband had divorced her in a few abrupt words, even as Herod cast forth his own wife, a young princess of the desert. Whereupon Herod and Herodias were married, despite the holy law which forbade a man to wed his brother's wife while the brother yet lived. And, in truth, the deed was a matter of shame to the Jewish people, seeing that such a marriage was both incestuous and ungodly in their eyes. Yet none dared lift his voice against it, save only John the Baptist.

Like an unkempt hermit of ancient days, he came raging out of the desert, his shaggy head held high, his eyes ablaze with fury. And even as the prophet Nathan had reproached King David with Bathsheba, and as Elijah had reproached King Ahab with the pagan Jezebel, so now the wrath of the Lord was thundered forth by this man of the wilderness.

"It is not lawful that you should have your brother's wife!"

What Herod Antipas had answered, none could say. Yet those who heard the tale were stricken with fear for the prophet who had risen up against a ruler favored by Rome.

While they spoke together, the light of the declining sun faded from the court, the leaves, the tendrils of the vine, the clustered grapes, even the great clay water jars became patterns, sharply black, against the soft green dusk. Within the shop, James and Jude laid aside the tools of their labors, swept the floor of the curled shavings, the sawn dust, the fallen wedges and fragments and splinters of the new wood. And when they had come from the shop, their mother rose and went forth with them to the duties of her own household . . . the kindling of the lamps, the bringing of water in which her sons might cleanse themselves of dust and sweat, the serving of the pottage simmered in the coals.

She besought Mary to break the evening bread with them, but Mary answered that she would await another time. For she said to herself: I would not have him return to an empty room, a cold hearth, a board barren of food. . . . Yet when they had departed, the sound of their mingled steps fading into the silence, she was stricken with loneliness.

For many days, all had been in readiness for his coming, as now: the swept room, the filled lamps, the brimming water jars, the drying linens he would take into his hands when he

142

had bathed, the cleanly garments in which he would garb himself, the honey cake which had delighted him since the days of his childhood, kneaded and baked that morning, and saved carefully against his return.

And she went and stood in the doorway and gazed beyond. The moon was high and radiant, the street glimmering and still, empty save for a pale pariah dog sniffing along the door-posts. And she said to herself: It may be that he will come even yet. Though the hope was forlornly voiced, and without actuality.

She had taken no food, nor did she desire it. Thus she seated herself near the lamp and lifted the unfinished garment, plying the needle, the colored threads. The silence of the house was of such intensity that small and trivial sounds became intrusive and startling: the shrill chirping of a cricket near the door, the quiet breaths of the sleeping ewe in the outer court, the disorderly flight of a moth seeking the kindled flame. And now her heart cried out, even as on the night when she and Joseph had turned back to Jerusalem, seeking the lad, "Oh, my son . . . where are you in this unhappy hour?"

For what cause was he detained more than forty days on a journey to be accomplished in six? Surely some evil had befallen him. In the regions of desolation near Jericho, even caravans were set upon by outlaws rising suddenly from paths one would believe incapable of concealing a viper. Here, many a lone traveler had been robbed and slain, his goods and donkey seized, his broken body hurled into the depths of a gorge where only the vultures would seek it out. . . .

But she cast the fearful image from her, seeking to fasten her thoughts upon the embroidery in her hands. In truth, the hour was late, and many of the village slumbered, yet she did not cease her slow and even stitching. At length, she finished the garment, gazed upon it, folded it carefully and put it aside, her needle thrust through the fabric, the lengths of thread laid neatly upon it. There is no need to wait longer, she thought desolately, and it appeared that the room had grown chill, the lamp pale and wavering, the honey cake stale, its flavor spent.

Then, suddenly, there was a step on the path beyond, and her son stood in the doorway. His face was darkened by the heat of the sun, his garments begrimed by the dust of the journey, yet his arms were held forth to receive her, his lips framed the tenderest word in the whole of their language: *"Woman . . ."*

And she ran to him, crying out his name, her voice shattered by the strength of her gladness.

"You have been so long away. . . ."

He answered quietly.

"I would not have my mother distressed for me."

And, even as he uttered the words, she recalled how it was that he had turned to her in the temple, saying, "Did you not know I must be about my Father's business?"

Then she hastened to bring forth all that she had made ready for this hour, the water of his cleansing, the garments redolent of wind and sun . . . to kindle the lamps, that the room might have the radiance of her spirit, to spread forth the festive meal. And when he had offered the prayer before food, they ate together, while he smiled to see the dishes most pleasing to his heart.

Afterward, he told her how it was that he came upon John, his cousin, baptizing in the waters of the Jordan all whose hearts would be cleansed of the stain of sin. There was a vast throng gathered about him, and Jesus stood among them, a young Galilean, tall and still, clad in a common tunic, a cloak with the usual tassels, a man not unlike many of the multitude. Yet when he went forward, even as the others, the Baptist drew back, gazing upon him with the mystic eyes of a prophet.

"Wherefore have you come to be baptized of me?" he asked.

144

And, speaking in tones of deep humility, he added, "It is I who have need to be baptized of you."

Then Jesus said quietly, "Let it be so . . . for thus it becomes us to fulfill all righteousness."

And entering the waters, he was baptized by the son of Zacharias.

Afterward, being filled with the holy spirit, he went forth into the desert, that he might be alone with the Lord. And it was here that he dwelt forty days and nights, fasting.

The nature of this wilderness was well known to all of Nazareth, for many were the tales of its desolation. It was a place of unending hills and steep, barren ridges . . . of crumbling limestone and rock-strewn slopes, wherein the unbroken silence afflicted the ears and burdened the spirit. Thin and winding paths led to the mouths of caverns filled with darkness, dwelling places of hermits and brigands, the lairs of wild beasts. As far as the eye of man could discern, there was nothing to be seen save the parched and shattered hills, the broken cliffs, the tumbled stones . . . a region of wild loneliness which had been a refuge to many in the history of Israel. Here David had fled from the armies of Saul, and Elijah from the wrath of Jezebel. Here many a desert prophet had heard the voice of the Lord rising from the lingering silences.

And so it had been with her son, Mary thought. She thought of his seeking, by day, the shelter of a cavern, the shadow of a rock. And, by night, gazing up at the numberless falling stars, beholding the mists that rose, in eerie desolation beneath the moon, from the shores of the Dead Sea, hearing the lonely cries of lions and jackals in the echoing distance.

Then, lifting up his heart to the Lord, and his eyes to the radiance of the heavens, surely he had dwelt upon the words of another prophet of Israel, the shepherd Amos, whose songs of praise had been offered upon the altar of this same wilderness.

"Lo, He that forms the mountains and creates the wind, that brings forth the morning darkness, and treads the high places of the earth, the Lord is His name. Seek Him that made the seven stars and Orion, that turns the shadow of death into morning and makes the day dark with night, that calls forth the waters of the sea and pours them out upon the face of the earth. The Lord is His name."

And she knew it was there, beneath the high loneliness of the stars, that the Lord had revealed to him the nature of his destiny.

For when the forty days had ended, he understood the measure of his power. And, being hungered by reason of his unbroken fast, he was tempted to command that the stones in the dust before him become bread. Yet it was known to him that he was to minister to others, and not to himself. Thus he turned from the stones, recalling the syllables of an ancient Jewish law: "Man does not live by bread alone, but by every word which comes forth from the mouth of God."

And, clambering still higher amid the fastness of the wilderness, he perceived that even though he cast himself down from the uttermost summit, no harm would befall him, seeing that he had not fulfilled his destiny. Yet he put the thought from him, knowing he was chosen that he might glorify God, and not himself.

Standing upon the rugged mountain, it was as though he beheld all the kingdoms of the earth in a moment of time. And, gazing upon them, he was tempted by an intrusive spirit of evil, to seize them for himself. Yet it was known to him that his kingdom was not of this world, and power was given him only that he should do the will of the Lord.

Thus he had come forth from the wilderness unsullied and inviolate.

Afterward, he and John had spoken together in quiet communion, knowing themselves brethren. And he had looked

146

upon still another kinsman, the young John, son of Zebedee, who had come forth with his friends, Peter and Andrew, to hear the word of the Baptist. They had traveled northward together until he left them at a crossing of the ways, that he might behold his mother's face before he fulfilled his promise to visit them in Bethsaida, on the lake.

"Yet I will go forth to them in another day. . . ."

She turned to him in swift concern.

"What of the marriage of Jerusha . . . seeing that the time is almost upon us? Truly it will be a day of sorrow in her eyes, if you are not numbered among the guests."

He smiled.

"Say to Jerusha that I will eat of her wedding feast."

A silence fell between them. Then he lifted her hand and held it within his own, gazing upon her with quiet eyes. And he told her, then, that as he prayed in the wilderness, the Lord had made known to him all that would befall him.

With another day, he would go forth to the cities of the lake, and never again would he dwell within the walls of Nazareth. It was known to her that his destiny was upon him. And she said in her heart: The Lord is my refuge and my strength. Let it be done to us according to His word.

XVII.

THEY WENT UP TO CANA TOGETHER, SHE AND MARY CLEOPHAS and the sons of Mary Cleophas, save Simon who would not abandon the tending of his fields and vineyards for the sake of revelry, and Joses, who dwelt with him. And they bore, upon the back of the donkey and among their own burdens, many things for the wedding feast: newly ground meal, skins of wine and oil, eggs and honey, sweetmeats and olives. There were also fragrant ointments for the adornment of the bride and the fair wedding tunic, as well as certain gifts for the household of Jerusha and Abner: low stools shaped by the hands of James and Jude, a small and perfect cradle, a handsome clay lamp from the village potter, a pair of kids with which to begin a flock.

Cana lay against a rising hillside some miles north of Nazareth, a pleasing village of flat white dwellings and cleanly streets in the broad shade of numerous fig trees. Here certain cousins of Mary and Mary Cleophas had dwelt for unremembered generations and here the youngest among them, daughter of the widowed Rizpah, would wed the village smith.

In every Galilean village, a wedding was a matter of rejoicing, a festivity of merriment and uncommon abundance wherein a man might put aside, for a little time, the rigors and sorrows of his uneventful days. Thus all would come forth to honor the joyous couple, to partake of the spread feast, to

148

drink of the wedding wine, join in the marriage songs and music and dances deep-rooted in time. Even the young daughters of Mary Cleophas, and their husbands also, would journey up to Cana on the evening of the marriage rites.

Seeing that a wedding was a costly thing, they who were kinsmen brought forth treasured finery to be loaned to both bride and groom, that they might appear seemly in the eyes of all who looked upon them. And those who were bidden to the feast came, not empty-handed, but bearing worthy delicacies for the festive table.

The wedding would take place on a Wednesday, this being the proper day for a virginal bride. Thus, when Mary and Mary Cleophas had come within the house of Rizpah, had joyously embraced her, and her daughter also, they turned to the matter of preparations with little time to be spared.

According to the custom, the feast would be spread forth, not in the house of Jerusha, nor that of the groom, but in the home of a friend dear to the heart of the family. Thus it was Deborah, a neighbor of both means and generosity, who would welcome the guests.

Even as she entered the village, Mary came upon friends stricken with disappointment that her son was not at her side, for there were none who did not regard him with uncommon affection. Indeed as she and the others approached the well of the village, Jerusha herself, lifting a red clay jar to her shoulder, cried out for word of her beloved cousin. And those nearby murmured among themselves, at once astonished and dispirited that Jesus was not to be seen. Yet when Mary hastened to say that he would follow after, they were both appeased and joyous.

Jerusha was a little past the fourteenth year of her life, small and merry, and by reason of her youth and happiness, pleasing to look upon. It was in haste and anxiety that she and her mother toiled for several days, with Mary and Mary Cleophas and certain village women and girls, accomplishing all that was required in the house of Deborah. Yet, by reason of their pleasing companionship, they turned to the numberless tasks with great lightness of heart.

On the afternoon of the chosen day, when the last long, unbroken rays of reddened light lay upon the plain beyond, the two women of Nazareth and certain of the young maids set about the ritual bathing of the bride in warm and scented water. Afterward, they anointed the whole of her spare young body with such a profusion of fragrances as to be wafted along the street by the wind of evening. Whereupon they brushed and perfumed her hair, garbed her in the wedding tunic of rich and beautiful embroidery, fastened upon her feet exquisitely wrought sandals from the wedding chest of a neighbor. And she was adorned in further finery gladly borrowed, generously loaned: rings and earrings, necklaces and armlets, anklets and amulets, wedding veils gossamer thin. A marriage girdle was knotted at her waist, while the oldest woman spoke words which desired for her the glory of all women, motherhood. Then, gazing upon her as she stood ready for the going forth to her groom, those of the bedchamber embraced her and wept . . . out of their happiness that this unforgettable day had come to her . . . out of their sorrow for the passing of her light, unburdened years . . . out of their own remembrances. And there were some, such as Mary, whose tears were shed for one long closed within the dust of the grave.

Dusk had fallen upon the village, the plain lay black and empty beyond the windows open to the soft spring night, the distant hills gleamed in the light of the waxing moon. Mary and Rizpah and Mary Cleophas waited, in festive tunics and veils, with the young bride and her maidens. Then, suddenly, the sound of pipes and tabors and cymbals came to their ears, distant and then nearer, mingled with clear young voices lifted in a known song. A gathering of merry youths, companions of the groom, had come to bear Jerusha to the house of Deborah in the festive carrying chair used by all the brides of Cana.

According to the custom, when they had halted before her, with many cries of admiration for her beauty, they led her and all of her house in a joyous marriage procession, the singing of other marriage songs, the shrilling of the pipes, the beating of the tabors, the clashing of the cymbals. And many ran from their dwellings that they might behold the merry-hearted scene.

The first to walk forth were the companions of the groom, save those who bore the poles of the chair upon their shoulders, clearing a passage with laurel boughs, chanting again and yet again, "Make way for the bride!" Following after them were her own companions, seven maidens who held lighted lamps in their hands, for the way was dark, even in the glimmering of the risen moon. After the bride walked her kinswomen, followed by certain elders who bore a cock and hen, symbols of fertility.

Near the marriage canopy which had been raised in the house of Deborah stood the steward of the feast, one who directed the festivities of the evening for a considerable sum. Indeed, his price was greater than the purse of a poor man could bear, yet Abner had summoned and paid him, desiring to do honor to his bride. It was said that Abner had labored unceasingly for only a little less than two years, putting aside every coin, that he might provide Jerusha with a worthy house and a seemly wedding day. Mary knew how carefully and with what anxiety he had counted the cost of the steward, the wedding wine, and the evening meal with his companions which was the duty of every groom.

And now, seeing that this meal awaited them, the youths who had borne Jerusha to the house of Deborah departed to that of Abner, wherein they would remain, eating and drinking and jesting together, until such a time as it pleased them to come forth to the rites of the marriage. And who could say when this would be? Certain grooms who had clamored to claim their brides lingered at their own suppers until past the hour of midnight. Others, quiet and solemn men who had shown no impatience for marriage, scarcely waited until their guests had eaten before rising and seeking to the beloved. Yet who was to say when any bridegroom would come?

The house of Deborah was radiant with lamplight, fragrant with the smell of blossoming boughs which adorned the walls and framed the doorways. At the entrance had been placed six large jars of water, that the guests might purify their hands before going in to the feast. Deborah herself, a kindly woman generous of heart, had spread forth small delicacies to stay the hunger of the women and maidens who waited in the company of the bride. These they tasted idly and without hunger, as they sought to pass the unfruitful hours with light and merry words. And certain of the maidens told of grooms so long delayed that the oil in the lamps was spent, the feast beyond restoring, and the bride asleep.

Yet Abner was not such a one as to delay his own marriage while companions took their pleasure in coarse songs and immoderate drinking. Thus, when they had eaten a seemly portion, he rose from the table and departed from the house. The companions of his youth walked with him and, in the light of the torches they bore, he was a figure comely to behold, walking with a lordly stride, clad in a fair white robe with a wreath of laurel upon the gleaming blackness of his hair.

And now the steward of the feast hastened to Jerusha, crying out, "Behold, the bridegroom comes!" Whereupon her maidens, kindling their lamps, went forth to meet him singing the ancient song: "*I will rise now . . . and go about the city in the streets . . . and in the broad ways, I will seek*

152

him. . . ." And when they had come upon him, they turned back that they might walk beside him, even to the canopy of marriage, and when any came forth from their houses on the way, he cast handfuls of sweetmeats before them.

Now, the rites of the marriage would be brought about. A multitude of bidden guests, following after the groom, surged within the house of Deborah. And suddenly, lifting her eyes to those who entered, Mary beheld her son garbed in seemly white, bearing a laurel branch in his hand, smiling into her eyes across the heads of those who stood between. And she perceived, in his company, two youths who were strangers in her eyes. Yet both were known in Cana, for Nathanael had been born in this village and often came here to visit his kinsmen, at times with Philip, his companion. Afterward, when the rites of marriage were ended and the feast begun, Jesus brought his companions to her, saying how it was that they had journeyed together from Bethsaida.

And now all of the company turned to the delicacies set forth for their delight. In truth, there were few among them who had not suffered hunger in the weary hours of waiting, and the men of Galilee, being laborers and fishermen and tillers of the land, possessed mighty appetites in any season. Thus, the food and drink which had seemed abundant for three times the number of the guests was swept from the table as though by some sudden and despoiling storm. And suddenly Mary beheld the good Deborah approaching her with unconcealed distress, seeking her counsel in a matter of anxiety.

"Behold," she whispered, "there is no more wine. . . ."

It was not to be believed, yet the jars stood empty, even while the guests awaited the filling of their bowls. And gazing upon the stricken face of the groom, Mary's heart went forth to him in pity, as she recalled how he had labored for this day.

Thus, moved by his wretchedness, she turned from him and went forth to her son, who sat a little distance apart, with the two from Bethsaida. And she said to him quietly, "They have no wine."

For the space of a moment, he was silent, even though her meaning was known to him, her desire revealed. Then, speaking gently, he answered, "Woman, what have I to do with you? My hour is not yet come."

And she said to herself: He is recalling the wilderness wherein he was tempted to use unworthily the power bestowed upon him by the Lord. Yet surely there is no unworthiness in sparing from mockery such a one as Abner, who walks in honor and righteousness before the holy laws. To be without abundance for the wedding guests was no small matter of shame. Such a humiliation would depart neither from him, nor from his bride, in the length of a lifetime. Thus she was certain in her heart of the compassion of her son.

And so, beckoning two of the servants of Deborah, she said to them, "Whatever he commands you to do, let it be done."

And now she was aware that the young men who sat beside him, Philip and Nathanael, were gazing in wonder upon her, and upon her son, desiring to know what was passing. Yet Jesus spoke only to the servants, saying, "Fill the pots with water." And they did as he commanded them, filling to the brim the six great water jars which stood by the doorway, and which had been all but emptied by the ablutions of the guests.

Then, seeing that the jars were indeed filled, he said, "Draw out that which is within, and bear it to the steward of the feast."

Whereupon the servants, astonished and afraid, bore to the steward measures of wine as beautiful as rubies, as sweet as a night in spring.

Then the steward, tasting, turned to Abner and cried out in syllables of pleased amazement, "Most men serve the good wine when the feast begins and then, when that is used, bring forth the poorer draughts. But you have saved the best until now. . . ."

And all the company tasted of it, praising it and honoring their host, so that the face of the young Abner was cleansed of shame, and his pride restored to him.

Mary turned and gazed at her son, smiling upon him with unvoiced love and pride, knowing that what had been done was for her sake also. And then she perceived that the youths of Bethsaida were staring at him with the dazed exaltation which comes only to those who have witnessed the presence of the Lord. And it was known to her that, henceforth, they would be counted not only among his companions, but among his disciples.

XVIII.

WHEN THE WEDDING OF JERUSHA WAS PAST, MARY HAD thought to turn back to Nazareth with the first light of morning, but her son would not have it so.

"Nay, let it be that you go forth with me to Capernaum, and abide a few days in the house of our kinsmen. Truly, Salome would rejoice to receive you, and to look upon the faces of our brethren."

Whereupon he laid his hands upon James and Jude and said, smiling, that they need not concern themselves with the carpenter shop for a little time. Nor were the sons of Cleophas unwilling to hear these words, seeing that they were in a festive spirit and had no desire to hasten back to the daily labor if, instead, they might go forth to Capernaum, which they had never beheld.

Thus they set out together, descending from Cana, away from the sown fields and terraced vines, passing down to the gleaming waters of the Sea of Galilee. Mary rode the donkey led by her son, and the others followed after, the sons of Cleophas, Nathanael and Philip, James and John. She besought her sister to accompany them also, but Mary Cleophas had returned to Nazareth with her daughters, for one was near the time of bearing and had need of her.

Capernaum was a city of fishing and trade on the shore of the fair lake of blue waters lying within a bowl of flowering shrubs and copper-hued stones. Here the leaves of lemon and pomegranate trees moved in the freshened wind, and the shadows were deep and cool.

To the south rose the white marble columns of Tiberius, capital of Galilee, a magnificent city built by Herod Antipas, and the gleaming gold turrets of his magnificent palace. Along the clear, paling waters of the harbor, near the gently rocked boats and many-hued sails, women of Capernaum spread fishing nets to dry in the sun. Fishermen, uncovered to their waists, bore great baskets of their catch to the places of salting and packing, to be sent forth to markets as distant as Rome. Publicans sat in their familiar booths, awaiting travelers and caravans. Those who possessed fields and flocks passed in and out of the gates. And though the city appeared to prosper, many who dwelt within it suffered unceasing want by reason of heavy tithes and taxes.

There was a large Roman garrison in Capernaum. One beheld the young legionaries in the streets and along the highroads, with their starched tunics and splendid bodies and arrogant bearing. Yet here there was little dissension between the conquerors and the conquered. The garrison was in command of one Marcus Serranus, a young Roman centurion who had turned to the Jews as to brothers of the spirit. And taking compassion upon them, seeing that they were too poor to possess a synagogue, he had built them one, out of his own purse, for he was a man of substance in his own land. It was a structure of great beauty, overlooking the blue waters of the lake, and many halted here that they might look upon it.

Zebedee himself was not unmindful of the poor, though he had never been counted among them. His house was large and pleasing, having a shadowed court, a fair garden, spacious rooms, even servants for the doing of the heaviest labors.

Salome, hastening forth to meet them, embraced the son of Mary with as great a measure of love as if he had been a son of her own flesh. And she cried out to all the company that to see them within the walls of her own house, gathered at her own board, sleeping in her bedchambers, had been the desire of her heart for many years. Indeed, she had more than once despaired of its fulfillment, for it was seldom that those of Galilee abandoned duty for the sake of a journey.

Mary found it a pleasing thing to linger with this cheerful and openhearted sister through three unburdened days. And there was much to be said between them, questions to be uttered, tidings to be revealed concerning their kinsmen. What of Jerusha, her wedding, and the young smith who had taken her to wife? And Rizpah . . . had she ceased to be afflicted with the trembling fever which had once come upon her, season after season? What of Mary Cleophas, her sons and her daughters? Was it indeed true that the disobliging Simon had wed a daughter of Nain? It was to be understood, Salome said merrily, that he would need to seek a wife in another village, seeing that his sullen temper was known to all of Nazareth. Yet James and Jude were pleasing youths, well-spoken and mannerly. And, perceiving that the lake was a wonder in their eyes, she urged them to go forth in one of the boats of her husband, that they might behold the ways of fishing and sailing.

Mary set her hand to such tasks of the household as Salome would suffer her to perform. They went side by side to the well, each bearing upon her shoulder an earthen jar. They sat together at the grinding of the flour, shared the making of flat round loaves, the paring of vegetables, the mixing of certain pastries. Nor did they cease to speak of the matters of their own lives, and the lives of those dear to their hearts.

Nay, they said, they would not go up to the Passover this year, nor would Mary Cleophas, seeing that she would be concerned with her daughter's new child. The Passover pilgrimage was the pious duty only of men, and though all rejoiced in it, women bereft of husbands and those burdened with small children often stayed within their own doors.

They spoke of him who was known as John the Baptist. Was it true, as Zebedee had heard, that he was indeed the son of their beloved cousins? All declared him a mighty prophet, some believed it was he of whom the great Isaiah had spoken long ago . . . *"The voice that crieth in the wilderness, Prepare the way of the Lord, make straight in the desert a highway for our God . . . and then the glory of the Lord shall be revealed."*

On the day before the return to Nazareth, Mary and her son walked together in the streets of Capernaum, that she might behold it fully, and along the shores of the lake. And when they had halted on the trodden path between the pale clouds reflected upon the waters, and the flowering oleanders which stood behind them, he turned to her and, gazing down upon her face, spoke to her gently.

"Mother, my hour has come."

She had known in her heart that it was so, that he would not turn back to Nazareth beside her, would never again labor within the carpenter shop but would go forth, with the spirit of the wilderness upon him, to preach the word of the Lord. And now she said to herself: Wherefore have I held the sorrow of parting to my bosom, nurturing it like a fretful child? It is not mine alone, but comes to the life of every mother, a cowering of the flesh, a desolation of the spirit, a wrenching of the heart. An unavailing regret: "Would that we might live again the years we have known together, seeing that I could minister to him more wisely than before. . . ." A sorrowful perplexity: "In truth, the years have swept upon us like an eagle upon his prey! Was it not but a little time ago I led him forth to his schooling?" A resolute and unwavering pride: "Until you come, my heart will be as empty as my house . . . yet these are words not to be uttered, lest they lay a burden upon you." There are women who would bind their sons with fetters of devotion more indestructible than iron, yet no worthy mother would be such a one. A worthy mother would see her child go forth from her, straight and unfaltering, upon the paths of men. Thus she said only, "I shall await you, my son," and departed from him with the blessing of their people. "And now may the Lord watch between me and thee, while we are absent, one from the other."

Thereafter, she was filled with a sense of loneliness, and a desire for the familiar comforts of her own house. Thus, with the first glimmering light of morning, she set forth from Capernaum, the sons of Cleophas beside her. And when they asked of her, "When will our cousin return to us?" she answered only, "Such things are with the Lord."

Afterward she learned how it was that he had chosen the first of those who would follow him and share the labors of his holiness. For there was no teacher in Israel who was without disciples, seeing that every rabbi was loved even as the High Priests were despised. In truth, it was the rabbi who labored to serve and counsel the people of Israel and who, even when he hungered and had not as much as a covering against the bitter cold of night, neither sought nor received money for himself alone.

Jesus had gone forth to the shore of the lake on a fair spring morning, and had beheld certain fishermen, Simon Peter and his brother Andrew, casting their nets upon the waters. Nor were they unknown to him, for they, with the young John, son of Zebedee, had come northward with him from the banks of the Jordan. Now, toiling together, they beheld upon the shimmering surface of the waters the white-clad figure of a tall young man who stood before the myriad greens of the shrubs, gazing upon them. And when they lifted up their eyes to him, he said quietly, "Follow me . . . and I will make you fishers of men."

160

Whereupon they abandoned their nets and their boat and followed after him, for it was known to them that John the Baptist had said of this man, "Behold the lamb of God!"

A little distance along the shore, where reeds rose up through the waters and pelicans swooped, on waves of hunger, to seize their prey, they came upon the two sons of Zebedee, James and John, who sat in their father's boat with certain of his hirelings, arranging the nets. And when Jesus called to them, they departed from the waters, their father and mother, and the riches of their house, and went forth with him they would call Master.

Then Jesus entered the synagogue of Capernaum and taught, and all who heard him were astonished.

A little time afterward, word came to Mary, through certain neighbors who had heard it spoken in the bazaars, that Jesus was teaching in all the synagogues of Galilee. She was made joyous by these tidings, thinking to behold him in Nazareth. Yet he did not come, and word of him was uncertain, some saying, "He is in Caesarea Philippi." . . . "Nay, it was told to me, by one who knows whereof he speaks, that he abides in Nain."

And now he had, among his disciples, not only the sons of Zebedee, James and John, and the fishermen, Peter and Andrew, but also Philip and Nathanael, who were with him at the marriage of Jerusha, for they had believed him to be chosen of God since that night.

Wherever he went, it was said, he was followed by a multitude which sought his mercy, seeing that he had healed many of Galilee, taking from them all manner of sorrows . . . fevers and wounds and blindness, the torment of seizures, the devils of lunacy.

It was told that a certain leper came to him, saying, "Lord, if you will, you can make me clean." Whereupon Jesus, having compassion upon him, touched him and said, "I will. Be clean." And the man was cleansed and whole, and went forth praising God and proclaiming the holiness of the man of Nazareth.

It was told, likewise, that on a certain evening, when Jesus and his disciples came within the house of Peter, they beheld Peter's mother-in-law ill of the trembling fever which seized those abiding near lakes and marshes. At once Jesus healed her, and she rose from her bed and went forth, in good cheer, that she might renew the fire and kindle the lamps and set meat before him, and before his disciples.

There were none among the neighbors of Mary who spoke of these wonders in her hearing. In truth, being kindly, they had no desire to shame her with word of the absurdities which had lately come to their ears. Yet it was known to her that numberless tales concerning her son were borne through the village, passed from tanner to cobbler, from shepherds to potters to the bearers of burdens, told in the market place and at the gates, whispered by the women at the well. At her approach, they fell silent and staring or, seeking to spare her, began to speak of other matters, with a zest false and hurried, not to be mistaken. She had witnessed the obstinate silence of James and Jude, when certain men entered the carpenter shop, inquiring with mockery, "What word has come from the worker of miracles?" She had looked upon the burning wretchedness in the face of the beloved Mary Cleophas. And she said to herself: Yes, surely they will doubt . . . until the truth has been revealed to them.

It was not known to her that there were men whose hearts were hardened and bitter against her son. Such a thing was not to be! One did not speak ill of a rabbi. He was a man of God, loved, venerated, entrusted with words of holiness to bear before men. Would any deny his teachings, look with hatred upon him for works of goodness and mercy? Nay, such a thing had never been done in all the history of Israel, save

162

by the ungodly, the Roman, the Samaritan, the Gentile. . . .

Yet there was a day when Simon strode into her house, from the carpenter shop where he had been speaking with his younger brothers, his dull face marked with outrage, his heavy fists clenched against violence, his voice shattering the peace of the dim and cleanly room.

"Behold, our cousin is no longer content with the life of the humble, but seeks to be known as a rabbi!"

She strove to solace, speaking quietly, laying a gentle hand upon his arm.

"Let us be thankful before the Lord, my son, that out of our family has come one who is a teacher in Israel."

He uttered a short and bitter laugh.

"Teacher? What knowledge could he bring to the world, beyond the use of a plummet or an axe? That he has proclaimed himself a rabbi is a stain upon us all. Behold, even the beggars in the market place laugh to hear of it! Yet there will be far greater shame upon us when he is seized by the authorities . . . for who among them would suffer a false prophet to live?"

She stared at him, grown cold before his words, and knew for the first time a shattering terror.

XIX.

It was said in the villages and along the highroads: *Rumor flies faster than an eagle.* Thus many tales concerning the son of Mary were passed among those who dwelt there, uttered with both astonishment and derision. Behold, they declared, each tale was less to be believed than the one before it. Behold, now it was said that even the authorities consult him in his wisdom . . . a certain Pharisee, one Nicodemus, going up to be taught of him. Truly, a story of greater absurdity had never been contrived. For it was known to all that the Pharisees, even while harsh and unsparing, were learned men who had given their lives to searching and preserving the holy laws. Had any witnessed Nicodemus taking counsel with him? Nay, for Nicodemus stole forth to him in the dark of night. Wherefore? That other Pharisees should not be roused against him. Nay, it was a tale weak and faltering, lamely put, not to be received.

There were other tidings far more credible to the ears of the Galileans who heard them. It was told that Jesus, returning from a feast in Jerusalem, had come, not by way of the Jordan, but through the land of the Samaritans, even though it was a place of danger and he was utterly alone, save for a few disciples. Nor did he scorn the ancient enemies of his people, but dealt with them as a brother. Indeed, they gathered to hear the words of his mouth and even besought him to remain

164

with them, which he had done for a space of two days. And, hearing this, those of Nazareth murmured sullenly among themselves, for it was not seemly that a son of Israel should seek the ungodly.

From village to village he had walked, with followers and disciples, had come even to Cana, taught in the synagogue there, embraced his kinswoman Rizpah, sat at the board of the young Jerusha and her husband. And it was on the evening of that day that Abner, hearing a knock upon the doorposts, was astonished to behold at the threshold a nobleman attended by slaves.

Uncertain and wondering, he had stammered forth, "Whom do you seek?"

Whereupon the man answered, "Jesus of Nazareth. It was told to me that he would pass the night in this house. . . ."

Then, beholding the son of Mary, the stranger cast himself down, his rich garments gleaming in the lamplight of the humble room, and cried aloud, "Lord, have mercy upon my son, for he is stricken by a grave illness, and unless you come to Capernaum and heal him, he will surely die."

Jesus said to him, speaking quietly, "Except I show you signs and wonders, you will not believe in me."

But the man besought him weeping, "Lord, come down before my child dies."

Then Jesus, having compassion on him, answered, "Go your way. Your son lives."

The man departed joyfully. Afterward, there came servants of his house, hastening to meet him, declaring, "Your son lives!" And when they told him at what hour the child was restored, he perceived it was the same hour in which he had spoken with Jesus. And, from that day, the nobleman and all of his house believed Jesus to be the son of God, as did many in Cana.

Indeed, there was talk of him throughout Galilee. It was

165

told how he rose and went apart, in the first tremulous radiance of dawn, to hold communion with the Father in heaven. He spoke in the synagogues and taught among the hills and in the plains and at the crossroads. He counseled his disciples, that they might worthily bear the word of the Lord, healed the halt and lame and blind and stricken, sat at meat in the homes of many, giving unburdened hours to pleasing fellowship with those who would speak with him. And many entreated him not to depart, but to dwell with them henceforth.

There was talk, also, of John the Baptist, and a great heaviness of spirit because of him. For speaking against the unholy marriage of Herod Antipas, he had been seized and cast into the dungeon of Machaerus, the austere palace above the strange and desolate shores of the Dead Sea. And by many he was mourned as though dead, since those who spoke openly against the house of Herod did not long survive their own words.

The seasons passed. The ripened grain was borne from the fields and trodden out on the threshing floors by the slow-paced oxen. Clouds ceased to rise in the sky, the dust of the earth became as hard as stone in the destroying heat of summer. One after another, the harvests were gathered in, the honey-laden figs, the flowing purple vintage, the blessed fruit of the olive trees. Then the earth was restored to fertility by the dark and drenching winter rains. When these had passed, the hills were green, white sorcery came forth on the boughs of the almond trees, the desert bloomed as a rose. And men went out to sow their acres with quickened hopes and bursting seed.

Then word was borne to Mary that her son would spend the following Sabbath in his own village. And she rose up joyfully to prepare for his coming, for after the way of mothers, she hungered for him unceasingly.

It was no matter of wonder that he desired to visit Nazareth on the Sabbath. She knew with what tenderness he must look upon the synagogue of his childhood, the years of his growing up. Here he had been presented, with his hand in her own, on the first Sabbath after the sixth anniversary of his birth. Here he had learned to read the words of the law, had laboriously copied the letters of certain scrolls, had recited the psalms and prayers and commandments. Times without number, he had prayed within the cool and darkened walls, had stood up to read from the Torah, as any worthy son of Israel might be chosen to do.

In truth, the synagogue was the heart of Nazareth, and with all other villages it was the same. Here the people gathered, humble and reverent of heart, to hear and learn the words of the holy law. Here they gathered also to take counsel together concerning troublesome matters, to pray for rain in the seasons of drought and famine, to give thanks in the seasons of abundance. Here the evil were brought to judgment, some being scourged, some cast forth entirely, according to the word of the elders.

Like all others, the Nazareth synagogue had its ruler, a certain man called Ithamar who directed the order of worship, cared for the synagogue itself, chose those to stand before the others and read the word of the law, or interpret it . . . though no worthy man was forbidden to speak.

One might worship in the synagogue after the eating of the evening bread, as was done by many of the faithful. Yet it was to the worship of Sabbath morning that the whole of the village went forth, washed and garbed in cleanly garments, that they might appear seemly in the eyes of the Lord, the men seated with their sons and brothers, the women and daughters apart, in their own gallery.

Jesus and his disciples entered the village quietly, after the fall of darkness, yet within the space of an hour, his coming was known to all of the village. Indeed, the tidings were passed

167

from street to street, hastened from doorsill to doorsill. "The son of Mary has returned. He is even now in his mother's house, and those who follow him also." It was not to be doubted that, with morning, he would go forth to the synagogue as in other years, and there was none who did not wish to look upon him. In truth, all would have thronged to his mother's house, had they not been rendered shy by the presence of the strangers. There were some, new to Nazareth, who asked in awe, "Is this not he who has healed the lepers and restored the blind?"

Yet others smiled, with the tolerance of the learned for the utterly untaught, saying, "Nay, such tales are the lies of camel-drivers and garrulous old women. He has been known to us since the days of his childhood, and has shown us no such wonders. Yet, seeing that he is a man of uncommon holiness, it is not surprising that he should go forth to teach the word of God. . . ."

That night, he and his disciples slept in the garden, resting in the warmth of their woolen cloaks, rising at the first cock-crow. By lamplight, since it was not yet day, they ate of the bread set forth for them. Mary had made ready the food of this day on the afternoon before, that the Sabbath might not be broken. For the same cause, she had brought vast measures of water from the well, and had kept the lamp burning throughout the night, that it should not be kindled on a holy day.

Philip and Nathanael she had known at the wedding in Cana. John and James, being the sons of Zebedee, were her own kinsmen. Yet only now did she look upon the kindly Andrew, the stalwart Peter whose utter devotion to her son stirred her heart. And, because she was the mother of their rabbi, they turned to her with a gracious regard akin to reverence, and told her many things concerning her son's labors.

In the early light, they went forth together to the synagogue, passing through streets where many awaited some glimpse of

Jesus. And when these had spoken with him and had found no strangeness upon him, they put aside such rumors as had come to them, declaring, "In truth, I said from the first that such things are not to be believed. . . ." And were at peace concerning him.

Now they recalled how it was that they had loved him and thronged the synagogue that they might welcome him. Then, seeing that such was the usual manner of honoring a guest, Ithamar, the ruler of the synagogue, asked him to read before them.

From the gallery, Mary and Mary Cleophas gazed down upon their sons, the tall Jesus garbed in a seemly white tunic, seated in the midst of his brethren, James and Jude and Joses, and their brothers-in-law. But Simon remained apart, near the door, nor did he utter as much as a word to the son of Mary.

The elders took their places upon benches which faced the congregation, their eyes downcast, the long white beards upon their knees. Whereupon the ritual service began with the chanting of the Shema, answered by the amens of the little ones. "Hear, O Israel, the Lord your God is one God. And you shall love your God with all your heart, and with all your soul, and with all your might. . . ."

There followed the eighteen benedictions, the words of instruction and of the law, the reading of the prophet chosen for this day. Going forth to the ark of God, the rabbi and the chief elders lifted forth, slowly and with reverence, the sacred roll of the law. Whereupon all the congregation rose.

Afterward, when the time had come for reading the last portion of the prophets, Ithamar called the name of Jesus, asking that he stand forth.

A murmurous sound passed among those who watched, and all leaned forward, gazing intently upon him whose name was spoken throughout the province and beyond. With quiet dignity, he lifted the prayer shawl about his broad shoulders and ascended the steps. Ithamar placed in his hands the book of Isaiah, a long roll of papyrus around a length of ivory.

Utter silence fell upon the congregation. Then lifting his voice before them, Jesus read, "The Spirit of the Lord is upon me . . . because he has anointed me to teach the gospel unto the meek . . . he has sent me to heal the broken-hearted . . . to proclaim deliverance to the captives . . . and the opening of the prison to them that are bound. . . ."

His tones, deep and compelling, faded, echoing, from the thronged chamber. Slowly, he rolled up the scroll, placed it in the hands of Ithamar and sat down. Those before him stared, taut and unwavering, awaiting what he would say to them. And, in truth, such silence was upon them that it was possible to hear, from beyond, the shrill voice of a cicada, the plaintive bleat of a lamb, the light stirring of wind in a tree near the door.

Then he lifted his eyes and, gazing upon them, revealed to them, *"This day is the scripture fulfilled in your ears."*

A murmur came forth from them, astonished and unbelieving. Such words were to be spoken only of the Christ, the anointed one to come! Wherefore did he claim them for himself? Aghast before such a measure of blasphemy, they turned to one another, asking, "Is this not the carpenter, the son of Mary . . . the brother of James and Joses, of Jude and Simon? And are not his sisters among us? Would such a one declare himself the Christ?"

Suddenly a man rose up shouting, "If you are he, then let us see wonders from your hands!"

Another cried, "A single miracle, and we will believe!"

Mary leaned forward, shaken and frightened, for the tones were of arrogance and derision. Yet, even as she watched, her son rose to his feet and answered in tones resolute and unyielding.

170

"A prophet is not without honor, save in his own country."

Now a voice called up to him, "If you performed wonders in the north, then do the same for us! Are we less worthy than those of Capernaum and Nain?"

Near the door, a man leapt to his feet, his face distorted by wrath.

"Others he may snare, but not the men of Nazareth!"

It was Simon, and he was echoed by cries clamorous and disordered.

"Are we to listen to the blasphemy of his mouth? Nay, cast him forth!"

"Cast out the false prophet!"

"Stone him!"

All manner of voices cried out against him, the young, the aged, the learned, the untaught. And now those of the congregation rose up as one man, with the son of Mary in the midst of them.

She perceived how it was that they had seized him, even as his disciples sought to stay them, how all within the synagogue surged from it, with tumult and shouting, in violence and outrage. She and Mary Cleophas fled from the gallery, thrusting aside the women before them, stumbling as they ran. Again and again Mary Cleophas cried out, "Behold, they will slay him!" and strove against the throng, sobbing aloud.

In the midst of the howling multitude, he was borne through the streets and along the path which ascended the rugged hill above the village. Then Mary, perceiving what aim was upon them, cried out, "God of mercy, they will cast him from the summit!" For it was known to all of Nazareth that any who slipped from the brow of this hill would crash down the rocky gorge to destruction.

She strove desperately to reach him, even as did his disciples. The mighty fists of Peter had flayed half a score from his path. She perceived Jude and James assailing one man and then another in their attempts to save him, heard Joses cry aloud, "Nay, nay . . . you know not what you are doing!" She saw how it was that Mary Cleophas seized one arm and then another, beseeching, "Nay, it is your neighbor, Jesus, whom you would destroy!" And then, astounded, she heard the voice of James, the son of Cleophas, cry out above the clamor, "You dare not slay him, for he has spoken truth!"

But none could halt the madness upon them. Even now they were at the summit, even now they would cast him down upon the shattered stones. . . . Mary felt a hideous weakness upon her, bringing her to her knees. . . .

Then suddenly, with a movement so swift as to appear light and without effort, her son wrested himself from those who had seized him and stood gazing upon them. And as his eyes condemned them, one and then another, they fell back before him, silenced and afraid.

Slowly, saying no word, he turned from the summit and from the staring throng, passing down the trodden way between the thickets, signing his gasping disciples to follow him. When at length he came upon Mary, he halted and lifted her to her feet and spoke to her with unhurried tenderness, as though they stood alone and apart from peril.

"Let us go forth to our own house. . . ."

Quietly, they descended the hill, his arm sustaining her, while those who stood below fell back from them in wonder. Yet she knew, heart-stricken by the thought, that Nazareth would never receive him again, that he had indeed been cast forth from his own village.

XX.

AFTERWARD THE ELDERS DEALT WITH HER KINDLY, AS WITH ANY mother whose son had been seized by madness, or possessed by demons. In her presence, their lips were sealed against his name. Yet she perceived with what hatred their thoughts went forth to him, their eyes as hard as date stones, their mouths fixed and unyielding. And they let it be known that they would have him remain beyond the village, even as the lepers, the disordered, and those convulsed by torments . . . for they feared him no less than these.

A few men of Nazareth were stricken by uncertainty, yet these dared utter no favorable word concerning him, lest they be cast from the synagogue. Only Mary Cleophas lifted her voice which, being the voice of a woman, was lightly heard. Out of the love and faith she bore him, she declared without wavering, "In truth, he is sent of God, and there is no evil in him!" And she revealed to Mary all that was said of him thereafter.

In Capernaum, it was told, there sat at the tollgate a publican called Matthew, who dealt harshly with the people for the sake of enriching his own purse, and brought many injustices upon them. Yet, in passing along the street, Jesus turned to him and said, "Follow me. . . ." For it was known to him that much righteousness had been sown among the evils

173

of this man, even as a harvest of wheat among tares, awaiting winnowing and fulfillment.

Then Matthew rose up and followed after him, and was counted among his disciples. And he gave a great feast for him before they departed from the city. Afterward, many who heard of the feast were angered, and asked of Jesus, "Wherefore do you sit at meat with publicans and sinners?" And he said to them, "Those who are whole have no need of a physician . . . only those who are ill. I have come to call to repentance, not the righteous, but the sinners."

Yet all looked to him with veneration, sought him out, followed after him when he went forth, hastened to meet him when they beheld his approach. Day upon day, he walked through the land, from village to village, along the shores of the lake, among the hills. Often he and his disciples slept beneath the open skies, knowing as brothers the shimmering dawns and waves and stars, the risen wind, the slow-moving clouds, the inconstant seasons. And, after a time, all knew of the man of Nazareth, tall and lean and pleasing to look upon, browned by long journeys beneath the sun, his gentle dignity, the wisdom of his counsel, the reaches of his compassion, the holiness of his heart.

On a certain Sabbath, he and his disciples passed through the countryside together, following the trodden paths which divided the fields of wheat and other corns. No traveler was forbidden to eat of the fields and, knowing this, they plucked and ate of the grains, rubbing the chaff from them. But certain men hastened to bear word of this before the Pharisees.

The Pharisees had long served as interpreters of the holy law. And, in reminding the people to remember the Sabbath and keep it holy, they had set forth such a tangle of restrictions as to make it a day of utter bondage. A man must not cast grain to his fowls on the Sabbath, lest some of it be rooted and grow, and bring upon him the guilt of sowing. No Jew

174

might kindle a fire or even a lamp without sin, such things being counted as labors. Sinful, for the same cause, was the driving forth of flies, the paring of fruit, the kneading of bread, the bearing of a burden larger than an olive. On the street a man might not use a staff to help him, even though he were blind, seeing that this was the bearing of a burden, even as the wearing of a nail in a sandal, a false tooth in the mouth. If a man were near death, or a beast of his stable in danger, they might receive aid, yet if a woman as much as knotted a thread, she was guilty of weaving and therefore of sin.

The rubbing of chaff from grain was named threshing. Therefore the Pharisees cried out before Jesus, "Wherefore do you break the Sabbath by doing what is unlawful?"

Whereupon Jesus answered, "The Sabbath was made for man, and not man for the Sabbath."

Hearing this, they were both staggered and outraged. Thus they watched upon him, to see whether he would also heal on the Sabbath, for they meant to accuse him of blasphemy before the elders, and before the priests.

On a certain Sabbath a little time later, he was teaching in the synagogue at Capernaum when there entered a man with a withered hand, an infirmity which often brought great suffering and want upon one who must toil for bread. Thus Jesus commanded him, "Rise and stand forth."

Whereupon he turned to those who were watching, and asked them, "Is it lawful to perform a deed of mercy upon the Sabbath?" But none would answer him.

"What one among you," he asked then, "if his sheep falls into a pit on the Sabbath day, will not lay hold on it and draw it out? A man is better than a sheep. . . ."

Angered by the hardness of their hearts, he turned to the man, saying, "Stretch forth your hand. . . ." And it was restored.

The Pharisees, outraged by his disdain for their authority,

now took counsel together, seeking to destroy him utterly. For they feared that he would rouse the people against them. Wherever he went, he was followed by multitudes, hastening after him, striving to touch him, asking his judgment and not their own. A man who could not be silenced by fear must be silenced by death.

That year, James and Jude, the sons of Mary Cleophas, departed from the carpenter shop and never again dwelt within their own village. Since the wedding in Cana, there had been a discontent upon them, an unquiet dreaming. Then, on a certain day, they came and stood in the shadowed courtyard where Mary and their mother had just finished the grinding of meal for the evening bread. And James said to them in simple and unstudied words, "We believe Jesus is indeed the Christ. Thus we would go forth from Nazareth and follow him."

With the dawn of another day, they embraced their mother and Mary, and set their feet in the first reddened light upon the caravan road, taking for themselves no goods save their own clothing, a few coins, and the bread in their girdles, though Mary asked that they bear, to her son and to his companions, certain uncommon delicacies which she had made for them, toiling until the late hours of the night.

Then Lemuel, the young joiner who had wed a daughter of Mary Cleophas, took up the labors of the carpenter shop. In truth, he found it a pleasing thing to call the trade his own, for until now, he had toiled for another. And, in return, he gave Mary, out of his goodly earnings, a sum past the whole of her simple needs.

It was now that Mary Cleophas, being utterly alone, came to dwell in the house of Mary, and they lived, as did all other widows of Nazareth, lives honored and uneventful and infinitely lonely.

That year, it was told in Nazareth, as in all the province of

Galilee, that Jesus, beset by large numbers of sinful and suffering, had chosen twelve apostles to labor beside him. They were men of great holiness and compassion, who sought to cast from their hearts their own mortal weaknesses, even as he cast torments from out of the bodies of others. Speaking Hebrew and the tongues of the land, schooled in the synagogue and its rites, prepared by Jesus and the words of his counsel, they were neither ignorant nor untaught.

Among them were the sons of Zebedee, James and the beloved John . . . the fishermen, Peter and Andrew . . . the humble Philip and Nathanael . . . Matthew, who had been a publican . . . Simon the Canaanite and Thomas . . . and a certain Judas, born in the Judean village of Kerioth, who kept the moneybag and attended to matters of purchase. And counted among them also were the sons of the joyful Mary Cleophas, Jude and James who, being younger than James the son of Zebedee, was called James the Less. And by reason of the wonders performed by these men, their names became known throughout the land, even as the name of their Lord.

From the slopes of a certain mountain, Jesus spoke to his disciples in the hearing of a vast multitude, saying:

"Blessed are the meek . . . blessed are the poor . . . blessed are the merciful . . . blessed are the pure in heart . . . blessed are the peacemakers. . . .

"You are the salt of the earth, you are the light of the world. . . ."

And the hearts of those who listened were lifted up from the dust, wherein they had been trodden by the contempt of the Sadducees, the condemnation of the Pharisees, the oppression of the Roman conquerors.

He taught them laws of love and not of vengeance.

"You have heard: You shall love your neighbor and hate your enemy. But I say unto you: Love your enemies, bless them that curse you, do good to them that hate you, and pray for them that despitefully use you. . . .

"For if you love only them that love you, what reward have you? Even the publicans do that. . . ."

And he taught them to serve the Lord humbly, without holding themselves above other men.

"Do not give your alms before men, to be seen of them . . . as the hypocrites do . . . that they may have the glory of men.

"When you pray, pray to your Father in secret . . . and after this manner:

"Our Father who art in heaven, hallowed be Thy name. Thy kingdom come, Thy will be done, in earth as it is in heaven. Give us this day our daily bread, and forgive us our trespasses as we forgive those who trespass against us. And lead us not into temptation, but deliver us from evil. Amen."

And he said to them, "Ask and it shall be given you . . . seek and you shall find." Then he spoke to them in the words of the ancient Jewish law of holiness. "Whatsoever you would have men do unto you, do you even unto them, *for this is the law. . . .*"

These teachings Mary received with love and pride, and cherished them in her heart.

It was told that when Jesus came down from the mountain, and his disciples with him, he entered Capernaum and saw approaching the young centurion of the Roman garrison, Marcus Serranus. With him were certain elders from the synagogue he had built for them, and they were greatly distressed for his sake.

Then the kindly centurion said, "Lord, my servant lies ill in my home, grievously tormented. . . ."

Whereupon the Jews who were gathered beside him, fearing that Jesus might turn from one counted among the Roman conquerors, declared in lifted voices, "Lord, this man is worthy. He loves our nation and has built us a synagogue out of his own substance. . . ."

And Jesus said to the Roman officer, "I will come and heal him."

But Marcus Serranus would not have it so.

"Lord, I am not worthy that you should come under my roof . . . but only speak the word, and my servant shall be healed."

Whereupon Jesus marveled, and said to his disciples, and all that followed after him, "I have found no faith like this anywhere. . . ." And he said to the centurion, "Go your way. As you have believed, be it done unto you."

In the same hour, the servant was made well.

A little time later, Jesus entered the village of Nain and perceived that a funeral was approaching, a sad procession moving toward a tomb which had been made ready beyond the walls. Upon the bier lay the body of a sweet-faced youth swathed in burial linens and fragrant spices. Walking beside him was a bent and toil-worn woman who wept inconsolably, her sobbing mingled with the plaintive notes of the flute-players who marched beyond, the cries of the mourners, and the unrestrained wails of the women who followed after. In truth, it was a scene of great sorrow and wretchedness, and a lad who perceived Jesus gazing upon it said to him, "She is a widow and he was her only son." His words bespoke utter desolation.

Then Jesus went forth to the widow and, having pity upon her, said, "Weep not." And even as she stared at him through streaming tears, he laid his hand upon the bier. The bearers halted, not knowing what had come to pass, and heard the quiet voice of Jesus command, "Young man, I say unto you, Arise." Whereupon the youth sat up and spoke, and Jesus laid his hand in the hand of his mother.

Those who watched were seized with fear and wonder, yet

they glorified God, saying, "A great prophet has risen among us!" And they declared, "God has visited his people!" and bore word of the happening far beyond the walls of that village.

This came to the ears of Chuza, a steward in the Jerusalem palace of Herod Antipas who was wed to a certain dark-eyed Joanna. And when Joanna heard it from the lips of her husband, she yearned to lead before Jesus the companion of her girlhood, one Mary of Magdala.

It was in Magdala, a small fishing village on the beautiful lake, that both women had been born, had grown to the years of marriage. But the heart of Joanna was distressed for the other, for Mary Magdalene suffered the affliction of the seven devils, which cast her, writhing and foaming, upon the earth. And she was rendered even more piteous in the eyes of Joanna for the reason that she possessed great loveliness of flesh and spirit.

Indeed, she was as fair as though she had been formed from a pale and beautiful clay by the hands of a gifted potter. Her hair, abundant and gleaming, was the hue of copper, yet her eyes, wide and thickly lashed, were as dark as charred wood from a watch fire. She bore herself graciously, possessed mannerly and considerate ways. Yet all of the village sorrowed for her, seeing that no physician could cast the devils from her.

A little time later, Chuza journeyed to the city of Tiberius, where Herod Antipas and his wife lingered in the fairest of their palaces, that he might take counsel with the tetrarch. Joanna, who traveled with him, went forth to the house in Magdala, just beyond.

On a certain morning thereafter, as Christ came forth from Capernaum, in the midst of a great throng, two young women approached him humbly, and not without timidity. Then she who was called Joanna besought his mercy, saying, "Lord, if you will but heal her who is as my sister. . . ."

And she made known to him that seven devils had for many years afflicted the fair young woman, who was even more piteous now than in her childhood, because her parents had died and she was without any save frightened servants to give her aid.

Thus, taking compassion upon her, Jesus healed the young Mary Magdalene, and both she and Joanna believed in him from that day.

Then Mary Magdalene said, "Seeing that I am of a wealthy house, let me give to his labors, and the labors of his disciples, out of my substance. . . ."

Afterward, she and Joanna and her elderly servant woman, Susanna, went forth many times with the throngs which followed after Jesus, ministering to him and to his apostles, out of the wealth of Mary Magdalene and the labors of their hands. Other women came to them, desiring to share in that which they had chosen, and were given places among them. Then foods rich in savor were prepared and set forth, garments fashioned and woven and mended, bread baked in the cool of the evening, meat and fish broiled upon the coals. And the burdens of Jesus, of his apostles also, were lightened by the hands of these faithful Galilean women.

XXI.

THE SLAVE GIRL HELD FORTH A RICH BRONZE MIRROR, PEAR-shaped, edged with carven blossoms. And though the wife of Herod Antipas stared within the burnished surface, her dark eyes were fixed, not upon her own image, but upon some vision of disquiet known only to herself. For a moment, she stood unseeing and unanswering. Then, made aware of the waiting girl, she gave a swift and impatient gesture, signing her to put the mirror aside.

"Go forth from me," she said, shortly.

The slave, a comely Nubian clad in blue sandals and a short blue tunic, moved back with proper deference, and went soundlessly from the room. Whereupon Herodias turned from the polished dressing chest, away from the numberless ointments and perfumes, pots of dye, bowls of fragrant powder, and went to stand at the casement, to gaze out upon the shimmering waters of the Lake of Galilee beyond.

For many days she had wrested with a measure of anger which rose and fell within her bosom on waves of hatred not to be stilled. And, in truth, they had risen higher and yet higher so that, at last, they obscured her vision entirely, save for one thing . . . the image of him who was known as John the Baptist. A thousand times she recalled how it was that he had stormed within the palace and, halting before her astonished husband, had denounced them both.

182

"It is not lawful for you to have your brother's wife!"

Now, as she gazed beyond the casement, she was blinded by the strength of her own rage, so that the blue waters of the lake receded before her eyes, bearing with them the distant sails of the fishing boats, and the palms which leaned against the white, risen clouds. She beheld only the accusing finger of the wilderness prophet, the unsheared head, the blazing eyes. How it is, she thought, in unrestrained fury, that a princely ruler and his patrician wife should be reviled by this wild and unlettered barbarian?

It was an incident without reality, not to be believed. Yet much of her life had possessed the same quality of strangeness, as though it were no portion of truth, but a fanciful tale recounted by a beggar at the gates.

Herodias had been endowed with a singular beauty, for her blood was both Jewish and Arabian, the latter being given to her heritage by her grandfather, the evil and unlamented Herod. Seeing that he held his power by courting favor with the Caesars, he had sent her forth to Rome itself, to be given learning in the palace of Tiberius. For it had long been the custom of the Roman emperors to receive the sons and daughters of eastern rulers in this fashion, knowing that children reared as Romans would possess Roman allegiance.

Among the daughters of Rome, white-fleshed and delicately formed, Herodias was a figure not to be forgotten. She possessed a dark and burning beauty as rich as the sands of the desert in the setting of the sun. Her hair, long and black and abundant, gleamed richly upon her tawny shoulders, catching up glimmers of color, splinters of light. She bore herself proudly, in the manner of the desert woman of whom her grandfather had been born and, being possessed of riches, went forth in garments of silk, that her exquisite body might be chastely covered and, at the same time, utterly revealed.

She had grown up with a daughter of the noble Roman

183

general, Germanicus, and there was the affection of sisters between them. In the palace, they had shared the same rooms, the same slavewomen, the same Greek tutors. They had sacrificed together before the altars of the Roman gods, mingled their cries of delight in the slaughter of slaves and beasts and gladiators in the Roman arena.

In her fifteenth year, a marriage was arranged for Herodias with Philip, a son of Herod, whom she despised within her heart, seeing that his spirit, unlike her own, was both mild and submissive. Yet, having grown to womanhood as a daughter of Rome, it was known to her that one need not have love for a man in order to become his wife, to bear his children. A daughter of Rome was wed at the pleasure or sagacity of her father, and might be cast aside by her husband as easily as a slave, commanded forth from his house within the space of an hour, by a few words scrawled on a parchment.

Thus she had gone, in the dawn of a certain summer morning, to be bathed and anointed by numerous slaves, garbed in the flame-hued marriage veil, led forth to meet her indifferent bridegroom, to lay her hand in his, to share with him the sacred cake, to receive the keys of his house, all the while thinking him a figure of absurdity, with the great wreath of blossoms upon his balding head, his toga drooping from his narrow shoulders like the garments of an aged crone.

She had borne him one daughter, Salome, a child with a rich beauty not unlike her own. And she had dwelt in Rome as any Roman mistress of a high house, attended by many slaves and servitors, going forth to feasts and sacrifices and revels, and to langorous hours of rumor and idle merriment in the baths of women.

She was past her thirteith year when her brother-in-law Herod Antipas journeyed to Rome to pay his respects to the emperor, and to dwell for a little time in the house of Philip.

She recalled how it was that, in the year of their meeting, he was neither corpulent nor gross, as now, but polished and mannerly. Unlike the thin and stooping Philip, he was a tall and well-favored man with the comely face and lordly bearing of the desert peoples. Like these, he was skilled in riding and hunting, praised for his use of the bow and the lance, a handsome alien striding out of a singular land in barbaric splendor. And there was between Herod Antipas and the wife of Philip a likeness of spirit which drew them together, a driving and unsparing ambition, an insatiable yearning for power.

Philip had charged her with adultery and dissolved their marriage within the space of an hour, even as Herod cast out his wife, a princess of the desert left behind in his own land. Herodias had thought to have her slain, but this was not to be, seeing that she had fled to the protection of her father, the King of Petra.

Herodias and the tetrarch of Galilee then went forth, with the young Salome, to dwell in Tiberius, the beautiful city he had built on the shore of Lake Galilee, and which he had made the capital, giving it the name of the Roman emperor, that he might win further favor at court. Here they dwelt in the manner of Roman nobles, disdaining the humble Jews whose tribute had brought the splendor of the city into being, summoning their guests from the high houses of Rome, and Caesarea on the coast.

Though her husband was a lesser ruler, he was lordly in the eyes of Herodias, and commanded for her such homage as was shown before queens. And she rejoiced in her heart, until the Baptist came forth to cry out against her marriage.

In Rome such men were slain, their tongues torn from them, their mouths stopped with blood. Thus she asked of her husband that this be done, nor did she doubt that he would command his soldiers forth to do the deed. Yet instead, he asked of her, "Wherefore? Is he not a just and holy man? And none can say he speaks falsely, for such are the words of the law."

And he uttered the words of the priests of judgment. "'If a man shall take his brother's wife, it is an unclean thing.'"

She stared at him, staggered by the answer which had fallen from his lips. And she perceived that even though he yearned to abandon the holy laws of the Jews, he could not depart from them. Whereupon a tremor of fear seized her and she said to herself: If indeed the Baptist persuades him against me, it may be that he will cast me forth, even as the daughter of Aretas. . . .

And she contrived to rouse him to his own defense, falling down before him, embracing him tenderly, declaring it was not for herself that she wept, but wholly for him.

"For the Baptist is rousing the people against you . . . and should this be brought before the emperor . . ."

The thrust was skilled and telling, for a ruler who could not master his own subjects was despised in Rome. Indeed, a tetrarch in whose regions an insurrection flared might be swiftly deposed, bereft of his powers entirely. . . .

"I will command that he be bound and cast into the dungeon at Machaerus," he said then.

Yet it was known to her that there was a vast uneasiness upon him, that he feared to turn upon a man of holiness. And even when the Baptist had been seized and borne forth to the desert fortress, the tetrarch had commanded that no harm be done to him. For months he had remained within the dungeon, chained by one hand to the damp and rugged wall, yet Herod Antipas had sent him an abundance of food and drink, a robe to shelter him against the chill of night, had even given leave for certain of his disciples to enter the palace grounds and confer with him through a narrow window.

Now it was borne to the ears of Herodias by a slavewoman that her husband had gone to the dungeon to speak in secret with the man of the wilderness. And certain of the slaves believed it was in his mind to send his wife forth, even as she had feared. . . .

Thus, standing beside the casement of her bedchamber, gazing into the misted beauty of the lake, she thought with bitterness: In truth, those who conspire together against any man must later conspire against one another.

And she said to herself: I will not suffer this prophet to live!

It was possible neither to bribe a soldier to slay him, nor a servant to poison his food, seeing that he was guarded by men long in the service of the tetrarch, chosen for their obedience and faithfulness. Nay, the man must be brought to death in a manner both subtle and artful. . . .

In a little time her husband, with his court, the lords of his province, and certain guests from Rome would go down to the edge of the desert to keep the feast of his birthday at Machaerus. It was a palace fortress strange and formidable, reached on one side by steep and winding ascents which passed between masses of ancient rock, above gorges and shattered stones. On the other side, the earth plunged thousands of feet downward, at the edge of the palace wall, and from the terrace one might look upon the vast and shimmering plain below, the streaming glory of the setting sun, the unutterable radiance of the desert nights. And it pleased the heart of Herodias to recall that John the Baptist, whose life had been spent in the magnificence of the wilderness, could not behold a single star from the dungeon where he lay.

The feasts of the tetrarch's birthday were rich beyond the telling, held in the vast pillared banquet hall made fragrant with roses and perfumes and smoldering incense. Here, upon gleaming gold platters, a thousand delicacies were spread forth, wines mixed in ruby bowls, poured into gem-encrusted goblets. And it was known to Herodias that, after the feast, the men would desire certain dancers to come before them. . . .

187

She recalled how it was that the tetrarch rewarded the dancer he found most pleasing. "Whatever you shall ask of me, I will give you. . . ."

Whereupon her eyes narrowed, her beautiful lips were stirred by a slow and contriving smile. Then, she said to herself, the maid shall answer, "The head of John the Baptist."

There was, in the household, a Bedouin slavewoman who, in years past, had been a dancer. And indeed her dances had inflamed the lusts of every man who looked upon her, so that her name was shouted in wanton songs of the tents throughout the length of the sands. Now she was past the years of her youth, grown heavy and lumbering. Yet she was not unable to school, in the same abandoned dances, a tawny young maiden richly formed, lithe and graceful and having a love of dancing . . . even as her own daughter, the little Salome.

And now, a new image rose before her eyes, and her heart quickened before the wonder of her scheme, the measure of her rejoicing. She heard the deep sound of the desert drums, the high wail of the flutes . . . saw the young figure whirling faster and faster to the abandoned rhythm of the sands, casting the veils from her polished shoulders, her rounded breasts, her gleaming thighs . . . falling down at last before those who watched, that they might feast their eyes for a moment upon her nakedness.

She, Herodias, would remain beyond the marble pillars, awaiting her daughter's return, having commanded her, "If indeed he should offer you whatever your heart desires, then come to me, for there is a thing I would have you ask. . . ."

And, seeing that he had made the vow before witnesses, what could the tetrarch do save send his executioner forth?

A vast burden was lifted from the spirit of Herodias, even as the yearning to slay this prophet of the desert glittered like the light of madness in her eyes.

"I shall gaze upon his head," she whispered hoarsely, "torn

188

and bloody, the eyes yet open, the face blue in death, the hair falling over the rim of the platter. I shall gaze upon it and laugh, and I shall take the silver bodkin from my hair, and thrust it again and again through the tongue of him who dared revile the granddaughter of a king!''

XXII.

Only in the season of the Passover had Mary and Mary Cleophas beheld such a multitude as thronged the paths and roadways to the city of Capernaum. Yet few went up to the Passover who were not whole and sound, whereas these travelers suffered afflictions without number.

There were carts pulled by quick-footed donkey or slow-moving ox, wherein men had placed, upon the piled hay, those lame beyond walking, ill beyond rising. There were men who bore their afflicted wives and children upon their backs. Mothers led sons blind from birth, lamed by broken bones never sealed together, stricken by the torments of lunacy, by demons which caused them to jerk as they moved, with arms and legs which had ceased to grow. There were travelers who suffered such a measure of pain as to sob aloud, to groan or cry out with every labored step, clinging to staves, to the arms of others. A long line of blind leading other blind was guided toward the city by a man with a twisted and useless hand. Two youths bore, in a carrying chair, an aged one whose hands and feet were cramped and twisted beyond the using. A paralyzed woman was borne in a length of sailcloth by her four sons. Beyond the road, and forbidden to draw nearer, were lepers who crawled over the fields and hills on hands from which the fingers were missing, who dragged themselves forward on the stumps of feet, who were without an eye, a lip, the end of a nose, a hand, hideous to look upon and past forgetting.

There were those who suffered no ills of the flesh, but afflictions of the spirit only, the forsaken, the betrayed, the sinful and penitent and sorrowing. And these were men and women whose souls hungered for the touch of God.

Mary and her sister rode upon donkeys led by Simon and Joses. Indeed, it was for the sake of these brothers, their bitterness and terror, that the journey to Capernaum was made.

A little time before, word had come of the death of John the Baptist, at Machaerus, the lonely palace on the rim of the desert. By trickery, Herodias had caused her husband to have the prophet's head brought before her on a burnished platter, the eyes yet open, the hair hanging over the silver rim, the face blue with death. And it was told by certain slaves that, beholding the bloodstained head, Herodias had laughed aloud and taken from her hair a jeweled bodkin and thrust it through the tongue which had denounced her before the world.

It was said that Herod Antipas, having honored the holy man in secret, now sorrowed for his death and gave leave to the Baptist's disciples to bear his body forth and inter it in a seemly manner. And he was stricken with terror, fearing the vengeance of both the prophet and the Lord. For his evil heart sustained many superstitions of the desert, so that he believed every owl and vulture a portent of vengeance to be brought upon him.

The tidings aroused all of Israel, and brought sorrowing upon those who had loved the Baptist, but only fear and anger upon Simon, the son of Mary Cleophas. He cried out that Jesus also would be put to death for his teachings . . . and declared the time not far distant. He had spoken against the Pharisees and Sadducees, he had denounced the tetrarch, had declared before all of Israel that certain priests in high places were hypocrites and sinners.

191

"He will be slain," Simon cried, "as all other false prophets of Israel have been slain . . . and his apostles also."

Then Mary Cleophas, who had opened her lips in swift defense of Jesus, was stricken into silence by fear for her two sons, James the Less and Jude.

"Behold," Simon cried, "a madness is upon him. . . . Is he not but a man? Wherefore, except he is mad, would he stand forth in defiance of those able to destroy his life . . . and our own . . . with no more than a word? My neighbors turn aside from me, knowing him to be my kinsman, fearful that they will be with me when the authorities seek my death. My wife weeps for her own life, and for the lives of our children. Wherefore does he have such beggarly concern for those of his family?"

Mary, desiring to answer him neither in haste nor without justice, heard his words quietly. Until now it had not been made known to her that the families of Simon and Joses— even the families of their wives—and their neighbors, were in terror of the vengeance of the authorities. Yet this was to be understood, seeing that when any man was seized by Roman might, his family might be seized also, and all of his house. Indeed, there were many innocent kinsmen of accused men who had been slain, tortured, cast into prison, their wives and children sold into slavery or slain beside them. Yet . . .

"It is known to all," Simon burst forth, "that he loves you beyond any other upon this earth. Therefore, if you would go forth to him, asking that he return to Nazareth and the shop he abandoned, cease to arouse the people . . ."

A tremor of fear came upon her, for to rouse the people was a thing forbidden by Rome, punished by flogging, even by death, if the accused man had spoken treason. . . . Yet Jesus spoke not of Rome but only of God. He was the son of God. How was she to lift her voice against so holy a destiny? She perceived that Simon was gazing upon her, that his heavy face

192

was filled with distress, his voice had taken on an edge of pleading.

"I will bear you to Capernaum," he said, "and my mother also. And when all has been arranged, we can return together and know peace once more. The multitude will cease to follow him, even speak of him. Our synagogue may even receive him again. Such quarrels are not long remembered. . . ."

She answered, "Nay, Simon, it is not for me to choose his destiny. Yet if you wish to go forth to him and tell him what has come to pass, it may be that he would counsel you regarding it. . . ."

"I have no wish to go forth without you, seeing that he will abide by your words and not my own!"

She gazed at him quietly, perceiving his anxiety, the measure of the wretchedness which had brought him to submit to the judgment of a woman. And she said, "Let us abide quietly for a little time. It may be that the clamor of the scribes and the Pharisees will cease. . . ."

But instead it was strengthened and fed until it roared like a grass fire about the homes of Nazareth. One and then another, her neighbors besought her to go forth to her son and beseech him to cease afflicting the authorities and bringing peril upon his own village.

"Surely he will take compassion upon the companions of his youth!" cried the tanner. And Mary strove against a bitter smile, recalling that this man was among the first who had sought to hurl him from the summit above the town.

Against Joses also, many blows had fallen. For speaking half a score of words in defense of Jesus, whom he loved, he had been cast from the synagogue. The daughters of Salome came, weeping, to say that the other women turned from them when they went forth to the well, that the other children stoned their small sons. The pleasant-spoken Lemuel, who labored in the carpenter shop, revealed that those who brought their needs

193

to him spoke hurriedly and hastened forth, lest they be in his presence when the authorities came to take him.

And now their voices lifted to declare, in tones venomous and seething, "Not for the sake of God does he perform these wonders of healing! Nay, he has bartered with some demon of evil, trading his soul for the power of bringing sight where there is no sight, causing the tongues of the dumb to speak, restoring flesh from decay. . . ." And truly such very words brought shudders upon the pious elders.

At length, even Mary Cleophas mingled her pleading with that of her family.

"Behold, my sister, all of Nazareth has turned against Simon and Joses and those of their houses! Let us go forth to Jesus, seeking his counsel. . . ."

And Mary, troubled beyond the telling, agreed that it should be so. Thus they had departed from Nazareth to lay before him all that had come to pass. Now, as they neared the Capernaum gates they beheld an even greater throng in the city, they perceived that to speak with Jesus would be no matter of ease, even for his mother.

About them voices were asking, "Where is it that he abides?" And other voices were answering, "Follow after those before you . . . for all seek him."

After a time, they came upon a house wherein a great multitude of people was crowded, each pressing upon the other. Some stood upon their toes that they might see beyond, some lifted children upon their shoulders, that these might look upon the face of the Master. With sun and sweat and weariness upon their faces, assailed by insects and thirst, even pain, they stood soundless and unmoving, drinking in the words of Jesus as though these were living water. Slowly, Mary and her sister, and the sons of her sister, edged within the great court, and now Mary's heart quickened with joy, and tears sprang to her eyes as the beloved voice came forth to her. Then, suddenly, there were other voices, the polished wily tones of the scribes and Pharisees roused by the assertion of Jesus that he taught the will of God.

"Master, we would see a sign from thee."

Whereupon he said to them, "It is an evil generation which seeks after signs. There shall be none given, save the sign of the prophet Jonah. For as Jonah was three days and three nights in the belly of the whale, so shall I be three days and three nights in the heart of the earth. . . ."

A little gasp went forth from Mary's lips, for the words had chilled her very flesh. Yet before her sister could ask what had befallen her, they were seen by a certain woman of Cana who stood near to them. And even as she pointed toward them with a trembling finger she cried out, "Behold his mother and brethren are here . . . and seek him!"

The word was passed forward on a wave of disquiet while heads were turned, and one woman thrust aside another that they might see the face of her who had borne the Lord. A man standing within the house whispered to one of the apostles, who turned to Jesus, saying, "Your Mother and brethren stand without and would speak to you."

There was a stir among those who watched, as both men and women pressed aside, even to their own discomfort, that a path might be made for Mary; for Jesus also, for surely he would hasten forth and take into his embrace this small and delicate figure clad in the black garments of a widow. In utter silence, they waited. Then his voice was lifted to them again.

"Who is my mother? Who are my brethren?"

Those who listened turned to him faces stunned and unbelieving. Was he not to welcome her who had given him life? A murmur of wonder and uneasiness passed among them.

Mary, having drawn near to him, saw him stretch forth his hand to the apostles and to the multitude.

"Behold," he said, "my mother and my brethren! For whoever shall do the will of my Father in heaven, the same is my brother and sister and mother."

Behind her, Simon burst forth, "God of mercy, he has renounced us!"

And Joses answered, striving to comfort her, "Say no ill of him who is mad. . . ."

Beyond the shoulders of those before her, Mary gazed upon her son, even as his eyes rested on her face. And it was as if she said to him: Behold, it was known to me, even as you departed from Nazareth, henceforth you would belong only to God. It was known to me that you would be bound by the ties of the spirit only. In the love of God, and of His son, is one mortal to count above another? Nay, for such love transcends the bonds of flesh. Yet out of all who have trodden the earth since the beginning of time, I am the most favored of women, for I have borne him who shall save the world, and all generations shall call me blessed.

Gazing into his eyes, she knew he yearned to come forth to her, even as she would have him do, yet should he do this thing, the lesson he had given those of the throng would be lost to them.

And even as there flowed between them the streams of their hallowed love and singular understanding, she turned from him, knowing he perceived that she blessed him, in the ancient words of the people, as she had done many times before.

"The Lord bless you and keep you. The Lord make His face to shine upon you and be gracious to you. The Lord lift up His countenance upon you, and give you peace."

XXIII.

THAT YEAR, ZEBEDEE DIED AND SALOME DEPARTED FROM CAP-
ernaum and journeyed down to Nazareth to linger for a little
time with her sisters in the house of Mary. And she brought
word to Mary Cleophas of her sons, James the Less and Jude,
who had done many wonders in the name of the Lord, had
learned to speak graciously and without reluctance before the
multitude. And the humble heart of Mary Cleophas was lifted
up in thanksgiving that sons of her flesh were indeed prophets
in Israel and witnesses to the word of God.

To Mary, Salome brought word of Jesus, how it was that he
passed throughout the land teaching in the synagogues and
upon the plains and hills and by the lake, healing both spirit
and flesh.

It was while he taught in Gadara, across the lake, that there
had come forth to meet him a man stricken with the demons
of lunacy. Indeed, he was of such violence that none could
keep him bound, seeing that he tore away the chains and burst
asunder his fetters. For a long time, he had dwelt in the wild
and blinded loneliness, among the tombs, wandering forth
into the mountains, crying aloud, cutting himself with edged
stones, suffering the mockery of men.

Coming to the Master, he cast himself down before him and
cried out, "I beg you, do not torment me!"

Jesus had asked him gently, "What is your name?"

Whereupon the crazed one said, "My name is Legion . . . for we are many."

Then Jesus healed him, and when those of the city came forth and found him clothed and seemly, they were stricken by fear of the men of Galilee and asked that they depart from the coast. When he went forth, the healed one desired to go with him, but Jesus said, "Nay, go to your friends and tell them that the Lord had compassion upon you, and healed you." And the man departed, to spread the tidings before men.

"It was while Jesus was in the city," Salome said, "that an illness came upon the little daughter of Jairus, ruler of the synagogue. In truth, it was plain before all that she was dying, and Jairus went forth to seek the healer of whom he had heard so many marvels."

The boat bearing Jesus and his apostles was even then nearing Capernaum. Striding through the throng that waited, Jairus cast himself down before the Master with his forehead to the earth, and besought him in broken words:

"My daughter is at the point of death. I pray you to come and lay hands upon her, that she may live."

Then Jesus went forth with him to his own house. And among those who followed after was a woman called Veronica. For twelve years she had suffered a bloodletting ailment which her physicians were powerless to heal. Thus, out of her faith in him who was Christ, she came timidly from the throng and touched the tassel of his garments. At once, healing came upon her.

Then Jesus, knowing one had sought him and been healed, asked "Who touched me?" Whereupon she came forward and cast herself down before him and said what she had done, and she feared his anger.

But he said only, "Daughter, be of good cheer. Your faith has made you whole. Go in peace."

At this moment, there came forth from the house of Jairus

198

a weeping woman who said, "Do not trouble the Master further. Your daughter is dead."

Already the sound of flutes could be heard, and the wails of the mourners, yet Jesus turned to the stricken father and said gently, "Have no fear."

And when they came before the house, he added, "She is not dead but sleeps." And though they laughed in scorn of his words, he went within the chamber, keeping beside him the leaders among the disciples, Peter and John and James, and the parents of the little one also. Then, taking her hand, he said, "Maid, arise!" And she rose, healed and smiling, and he commanded that they bring her food.

These and other works of Jesus Salome told, while they lingered beside the kindled lamp until the late hours of the night, speaking together. And Salome said that she would not return to the loneliness of her high house but would abide with them until after the Feast of Tabernacles, and then go forth with the women who labored for the sake of Jesus, to minister to him and to her sons.

The Feast of Tabernacles was a day of great holiness, the season of ingathering, when the year renewed itself, and thousands went up to Jerusalem to worship in the beautiful temple. The feast continued for a length of seven days, and was held in remembrance of the years when the children of Israel had wandered in the wilderness, dwelling in tabernacles, even as the tribes of the sands.

It was written in the holy laws that during the feast "ye shall dwell in the tabernacles seven days." Thus each family erected small and pleasing huts on the rooftops of Jerusalem houses, in the courtyards, around the temple, and upon the slopes, forming these from the branches of palm and myrtle and olive trees. Those who went forth to the rituals bore leafy boughs and offerings of fruit before the Lord. Only the men were required to keep the feast, yet many families went up with them, even as to the Passover.

Salome had said that Jesus would go up to the feast also, but he would go alone, and in secret, lest there be a multitude about him and his disciples. These he commanded forth to Jerusalem a little time before he departed from Galilee.

At no season of the year was Mary afflicted with so deep a loneliness for him as at the Feast of the Tabernacles, seeing that it recalled to her his childish delight in the small green huts wherein they had slept, and which his own hands had helped her to fashion. A thousand images of him rose before her eyes. She saw how it was that he would stride southward through the sun-scorched land, beholding the seared fields, the burning paths, the dry wells, the shrunken Jordan, the dusty stream beds. For the long summer drought was not yet past, and in the temple the priests would pray for the hastening of the winter rains.

Now she saw the solemn evening processional of the men of Israel, with the richly garbed High Priest going before, their torchlight torn and yellow in the wind of night, beneath the radiance of the moon. Yet whether her son would be among them was unknown to her. Salome had not concealed from her the danger surrounding him. A thousand tongues declared he would be taken by the scribes and Pharisees who sought to destroy him. Even Jesus believed he would be betrayed into the hands of men, for such had he uttered in the hearing of John, the son of Salome and Zebedee. Thus Mary was stricken with terror for his sake, and feared that he would go boldly into the temple to teach before those who gathered there, without heed for his own peril.

Afterward, it was told to her that he had indeed taught in the temple, amid the murmuring of many. Some declared openly, "He is a man of holiness." Some said, "Nay, he deceives the people!" Yet all stood in wonder before his wisdom, and there were many who cried, "This is the Messiah, the promised Christ!" Yet others, with derisive laughter, inquired, "Shall the Christ come out of Galilee?" Nay, the prophets had declared the Messiah would come of the seed of David, and out of the town of Bethlehem.

And they declared, "Out of Galilee arises no prophet!"

It was while he taught in the temple that the scribes and Pharisees brought before him a woman taken in adultery, thinking to snare him into denouncing the law of Moses which required that such a one be stoned. Thus they asked, "What say you?"

But he only leaned down and wrote upon the earth, idly and deliberately, uttering no word. They persisted, asking him the same question again and yet again, and at length, he said quietly, "Let him who is without sin among you cast the first stone."

And when he lifted his eyes, they had stolen forth, each condemned by his own conscience, and he was alone with the weeping woman. Whereupon he asked, "Has no man condemned you?" She answered, "No man, Lord." And he said to her, "Neither do I condemn you. Go and sin no more."

By night he slept in a tabernacle on the Mount of Olives, and each day, he returned to teaching in the temple, though it was known to him that he was in great peril from the Pharisees and from those who would witness for them, since they desired to seize him for speaking blasphemy.

Yet he gave no heed to them, and taught: "I am the Light of the world. He that follows me shall not walk in darkness, but shall have the light of life."

The Pharisees sought to deny his words, and he said to them, "I know from whence I came and where I go, but you do not know these things . . . you are from beneath, I am from above. You are of this world. I am not of this world."

Whereupon they commanded certain temple officers to

201

seize him, yet these returned without him, saying, "Never did a man speak like this man. . . ." And they were awed.

At this, the authorities knew even greater alarm, perceiving what numbers believed in him. And there were some who took up stones to cast at him, but he went out of the temple and lost himself in the throng.

On still another day, he came upon a man blind from birth and healed him. And the Pharisees said, "He is not of God, for he heals on the Sabbath." Yet others asked, "Can a man of evil do such wonders?"

Yet there were many who sought his death, and Mary suffered unceasing fear for him, thinking to hear that he had been seized by the authorities, and cast into prison even as John, the Baptist.

The winter passed, and with it the loveliest of feasts, the Festival of Lights, when flames were kindled in the Hannukah lampstand, when every widow in Israel saw reflected in the wavering radiance the faces of sons now grown to manhood and departed from her.

It was said that Jesus and his apostles were teaching beyond the Jordan, and no further word of them came until the season of spring. Within this time, his name fell less frequently from the tongues of Nazareth. Now that he was no longer within the province of Galilee, those of the village were less troubled concerning him. Men who entered the carpenter shop lingered to speak with Lemuel, unafraid. The women at the well ceased turning from the daughters of Mary Cleophas. Even Simon was appeased, and read from the scrolls in the village synagogue without fear that he would be cast from the congregation.

Yet in the spring, there came tidings of an unbelievable marvel which Jesus had wrought in the village of Bethany.

Bethany was but a little distance from Jerusalem, on the

Jericho Road, a distance which a man returning from the temple might walk in easy paces. Here stood the high house of one close to the heart of Jesus—Lazarus, with whom he shared a brotherhood. With Lazarus dwelt his sisters, Martha, a kindly widow, and Mary, a gentle spinster. Often when Jesus lingered within the house, Mary sat at his feet in the cool shadow of the court, hearing the words of his wisdom, seeing God through his eyes. Yet Martha, who would have neither hands nor feet in idleness, hastened in and out of the rooms, intent upon the cleaning of the floors, the kneading of the bread, the washing of linens, concerned with numberless matters of the household. Yet both were dear to the heart of Jesus, and it was not unnatural that they should turn to him in the hour of their despair. For while he taught beyond the Jordan, their brother Lazarus died.

When word of this was brought to Jesus, he said to his apostles, "Let us return to Judea."

Those who followed him did not wish it so, for they feared he would be seized and slain. Yet he declared he must go forth and, hearing this, the apostle Thomas said to the others, "Then let us go forth also, that we may die with him." For they loved him, and it was known to them that the Pharisees awaited his coming, meaning to destroy him.

When Martha heard that Jesus was approaching, she hastened forth, even beyond the village, and spoke to him in words of utter trust.

"Lord, if you had been here, my brother would not have died. Yet I know that even now, whatever you ask of God, He will give you."

Whereupon Jesus, stirred by her faith, promised, "Your brother shall rise again."

Tears gleamed in Martha's eyes.

"I know he shall rise again in the Resurrection. . . ."

Then Jesus, gazing down into her sorrowing face, said gently, "I am the Resurrection and the Life. He that believes in me, though he were dead, he shall live. And whoever lives and believes shall never die. Do you believe these things?"

And she said, "In truth, Lord, I believe you are the son of God which was to come into the world."

When she had returned to her own house, she whispered to her sister that Jesus awaited them. And Mary rose up and hastened to him, followed by all those who were gathered about her, mourning. When she came to Jesus, she fell down before him weeping, and Jesus wept also.

One of the mourners, knowing him to be the man of Galilee who had brought healing to many, whispered, "Could he not have prevented the death of Lazarus?"

Then Jesus went forth to the tomb, and all of the company with him. Standing without, he asked that the stone be moved from it, but Martha protested that her brother had died four days ago, a length of time for decay to assail his flesh.

Nevertheless, the stone was rolled away, and after Jesus had lifted up his eyes and prayed, he cried aloud, "Lazarus, come forth!" And the brother of Mary and Martha came from the tomb in his grave linens.

Afterward, all who witnessed this believed in Jesus, but others were angered, and hastened to the Pharisees to tell what had come about. And the Pharisees feared him even more, saying, "If we let him alone, all men will believe in him, and the Romans will take away our high place and our nation . . ."

Then Caiaphas, the High Priest, declared, "It is expedient that one man should die for the people."

The Sadducees also rose up in anger, for the deed in Bethany shamed them, seeing that they taught there was no life after death. And though there had long been enmity between the Sadducees and Pharisees, they united against Jesus, and sought together to lay hold on him.

Hearing this, he departed into the wilderness, and none could say where he might be found. Yet it was known to all that, being a devout Jew, he would go up to the Passover in April, as the holy law required of him.

XXIV.

SHE SAID TO HERSELF THAT SHE WOULD GO UP TO JERUSALEM
this year, in the season of Passover. For it was certain in her
mind that Jesus would keep the feast, and her heart went forth
to him in poignant yearning. It was a length of many moons,
barren and sorely troubled, since she had looked upon his
face.

I will go up, she thought, stirred to a trembling joy, and
Mary Cleophas also, to dwell with the others in the house of
Chuza. For Salome had sent word that while the steward
of Herod served in the great Jerusalem palace, she and Mary
Magdalene would abide with Joanna, his wife.

Times without number, Mary had lifted up her heart in
humble thanksgiving that these gentlehearted women min-
istered to her son and to those who followed him. And sorrow smote her, that she was not counted among them. Yet she
had no strength for the rigors of such a charge, nor would she
abandon Mary Cleophas to the full loneliness of widowhood.
Once Mary Cleophas had spoken of going forth with Salome,
yet this was not to be done, seeing that her daughters had
need of her. Yet she too yearned for her sons, and would gladly
go forth to the holy city, despite the wretched discomforts of
the long journey.

Thus they made ready their garments, the tunics and
sandals and girdles, the soft woolen cloaks and thin black veils.

206

They filled the small rush baskets wherein traveling Jews carried cleanly food when they passed through the province of Samaria, that they need not be required to eat in the manner of the ungodly. They cast upon the unresisting donkey the bundles of food, clothing and bed mats, the goods they would bear to Joanna, and to their sons: cruses of oil, skins of wine, honey, seedcakes, new garments woven with tender care.

As in years past, they set out from the market place of Nazareth, with those gathered for the pilgrimage. As in years past, there were some who looked upon the departing pilgrims with longing, some who went forth with them a little way. The wind was sweet on that morning, the shadows cool, the sun merciful. Thus they took pleasure in the flowering shrubs and ripening grain, the wondrous shapes and magical colors of the flowers of God. At night, they huddled near the warmth of their little beast, hearing the crackle of watch fires, the murmurous voices of the guards, the whimper of dreaming children, the snores of the elders. By day, they went forth again, heavy with soreness and aching unknown to them in the journeys of their youth.

Farther south, they departed from Galilee and entered barren land, shielding their heads from the assault of the desert sun, the thick grey dust. And, in time, they began the long and bitter ascent, seizing upon the last fragments of their strength. Then, suddenly, as in other years, the wonder of the temple appeared before them, and shouts burst from the throats of the men, even as shouts had burst from the throats of Cleophas and Joseph and Zebedee, in the unforgotten years of the past. And thus shall it be for all of time, Mary thought. Other seasons of flowering will come, and other feet will tread the long and weary paths to the place of the Lord. Other hearts will be lifted up before Him, other voices raised in hymns to glorify His name, for His mercy endures forever.

Then, as they entered Jerusalem, she perceived that there

were, within the streets, greater throngs than had ever before come up to keep the Passover. In truth, the city was in wild and tumultuous confusion, filled with the shouts of slaves and soldiers, the wailing of beggars, the cries of vendors, the tangle of pilgrims and goods and beasts, the flaying lashes of the Roman legionaries striving against disorder. The narrow passages were crowded with numbers not to be believed, and many among them appeared to be watching, expectant . . . gazing from the rooftops, peering from doorways, leaning from casements. Plainly some disturbance was expected, some insurrection feared.

Thus she and Mary Cleophas urged the donkey forward and strove to escape the pressing crowds wherein one might not take as much as a single step without treading upon one's neighbor. And, within a little time, they came to the house of Joanna, a stone structure of ease and beauty, with a flowering creeper upon its walls, a courtyard in the shade of splendid trees.

They were received into the house with cries of rejoicing and the plentiful embraces of Salome. Afterward, they turned their eyes to the women whose names were known to them, but whose faces they had never looked upon, Joanna and Mary Magdalene. And from the moment the girl of Magdala turned to Mary, she sought to serve and shelter the mother of him who was her Lord.

Then Mary, seeking word of her son, learned how it was that he had taught in the temple throughout this day, and now, seeing that evening was upon the city, would go forth to break the evening bread with his disciples in a certain upper room. Yet in the morning, they would lead her before him, would seek him in the temple. . . .

Afterward, Salome and Mary Magdalene set food upon the table beneath the arbor of the court. For they had no servant, Susanna having gone to spend the season of the Passover in the house of her son. Already the sun was descending into the waters of the Great Sea. A cool green dusk had fallen upon Jerusalem, and crickets had lifted their lonely voices in the weeds of the garden. Yet, across the deep valley, the mountains of Moab still gleamed with light. Lingering together, the women spoke of that which was nearest their hearts, the labors of Jesus.

It was known, even to the beggars at the city gates, that the priests conspired against him, and thus there were many who declared, "Nay, he will not come up to the feast!" Yet he had come, for what Jew would turn his face from his God for the sake of his peril?

He had come up to Jerusalem four days earlier, Salome said, and had entered the city riding upon the foal of a donkey, hailed in the manner of a conqueror. In truth, a multitude had thronged about him and hastened ahead, casting before him the fronds of palms, the boughs of trees, their own garments, crying out until the very stones echoed with the sound, "Blessed is the king who comes in the name of the Lord!" Whereupon the priests and Pharisees, hearing what had come to pass, were rendered white and shaken by the strength of their anger.

Afterward, he had entered the temple, that he might pray. And surely, gazing upon the marble thresholds, the splendid gates, the beautiful courts, his voice was lifted up in the words of the temple psalm so dear to the hearts of pilgrims. *"Blessed are they that dwell in Thy house . . . blessed is the man whose strength is in Thee . . . for a day in the courts is better than a thousand. I had rather be a doorkeeper in the house of my God than to dwell in the tents of wickedness."*

Then, when he had sought his disciples, he departed with them into Bethany, and lodged there that night.

With morning, he had come again to the temple, and had stood looking upon the long rows of tables where sat the money-changers. For though Roman money was used in matters of trade, only temple shekels might be used in the paying of tithes, the giving of alms, the buying of goods for a sacrifice. And for changing the Roman money into temple coin, those from the tables seized from these humble people sums no man dared protest.

Suddenly, beholding the measure of their iniquity, Jesus strode toward them and set upon them with a lash, driving them forth from their places, away from the fruits of their evil. And, with an unsparing hand, he cast their tables down, so that the coins clashed and rolled and were scattered upon the tiles of the floor. The money-changers fled in utter disorder and, striding after them, Jesus drove them forth from the temple, laying the lash about their fattened shoulders and flying heels. And when they were cast out, he stood gazing upon them and denounced them, crying, "It is written that my Father's house shall be a house of prayer, but you have made it a den of thieves and robbers!"

Then the old High Priest Annas, and his son Caiaphas, rose up in wrath against the deed, for their family owned the temple market wherein the money-changers sat. Besides the changing of money, they sold to the people vast measures of oil and wine and incense, the doves and lambs and oxen, all things needed for the sacrifice, at whatever sum they found pleasing. And they forbade that any goods of sacrifice be used within the temple save those from their own market.

It was known to Jesus that they meant to seize him. Yet, by day, they feared the wrath of his followers, and would have seized him by night, save that none knew where he would take his rest.

Then a certain elder asked him, "Is it lawful to give tribute to Caesar?" And it was a question slyly contrived, for should he speak against this, he could be called a traitor to Rome and brought to judgment.

210

But, instead, he said to them only, "Render unto Caesar the things that are Caesar's, and to God the things that are God's."

And seeking to charge him with blasphemy, a Pharisee asked him, "What is the greatest commandment of all?" . . . thinking he would depart from the teachings of his people.

Yet Jesus answered him in the words of the holy Jewish law.

". . . You shall love your God with all your heart, and with all your soul, and with all your mind, and with all your strength. This is the first commandment. And the second is: You shall love your neighbor as yourself. There are no commandments greater than these."

Whereupon the Pharisee said, "Master, you have spoken truth." And he declared that obedience to these commandments was greater in the eyes of the Lord than all burnt offerings and sacrifices.

Then Jesus answered, "You are not far from the kingdom of God."

Each day, he taught in the temple, in the midst of a pressing throng, among them women who held forth their children, that he might bless them. Earlier, the disciples had sought to turn these away, but he would not have it so, saying, "Let the little children come unto me, and forbid them not, for of such is the kingdom of heaven."

When these words of her son were made known to her, Mary's heart went forth to him with strengthened longing, so that it seemed she could not wait until the morning to behold his face. She recalled how it was that, in his boyhood, he had slept the sweet slumber of youth, his brown face pillowed upon one arm, his hair a disordered shadow, his face untroubled and serene. Her heart cried out: My son, my son, let me go forth to you even now. . . . Yet she said to herself: Behold, a night is soon spent. Thus, striving against impatience, she had gone with Mary Cleophas to the upper room. And, after a time, she fell into slumber.

Near dawn, she was awakened by a sound below, a knocking, muted and hurried, upon the doorposts of Joanna's house. A little time later, the voice of John was mingled with the frightened tones of his mother and, at once, it was known to her that some evil had come to pass.

Thus Mary rose quickly, that she might kindle a lamp. And when its wavering light had found strength and welled up into the darkness of the room, she perceived that she was not alone in her fears. Mary Cleophas had risen also, and upon them both there was an air taut and listening, a sense of anxiety confirmed.

Saying no word, they garbed themselves hastily and went forth, descending the stair, their hair in disorder about their shoulders. And gazing upon Salome, and the son of Salome, Mary cried out, "What has come to him?"

They hastened to her then, saying there was no need for fear. Indeed, it was nothing . . . even though the tidings might appear alarming in her ears. The authorities had seized Jesus in a certain garden on the Mount of Olives, had borne him before the High Priests, that he might be judged.

"Wherefore?"

"Since he has declared himself the Christ, they seek to condemn him of blasphemy."

Mary's lips moved numbly.

"What . . . what manner of punishment will they bring upon him?"

John turned to her, reluctant and disquieted.

"Who can say? Yet, seeing that they are Jews instead of Romans, they dare not send him to death. . . ."

"*Death?*" It was the voice of Mary Magdalene, who stood upon the threshold of a sleeping chamber beyond. "Wherefore is he worthy of death?"

212

"None has said he is worthy of death!" Salome sought to comfort her. "Behold, it is but a matter of questioning him. . . ."

Now Mary turned quickly to the troubled John.

"How is it that they found him? Did you not say he slept in a hidden place?"

Whereupon John told how it was that he and the other disciples had broken bread with the Master, in a certain upper room. And while they sat together, Judas, the disciple who held the moneybag, rose and departed from them. They had believed him to be going forth to a market, that he might buy food for the feast days. Yet, instead, his heart being ravaged by his own greed, he had stolen forth to the authorities, that he might lead them to the place of the Lord's concealment. For earlier, he had bargained with them, betraying Jesus for thirty pieces of silver, the price of a slave.

Then through the still blue shadows and radiant light beneath the paschal moon, Jesus and John and Peter had gone up to the Garden of Gethsemane on the Mount of Olives. Yet John revealed no word to Mary of the agony her son had suffered, knowing his hour was upon him, assailed by the terrors of the flesh, praying in great anguish of spirit, "Lord, if it is Thy will, let this cup pass from me. . . ." In truth, he could have fled into the desert and hidden himself in the wilderness, and escaped his enemies utterly. Yet it was known to him that this was neither the will of God nor the pattern of his destiny.

After a time, there was a clamor upon the stony path, a wavering radiance of torches lighting the edges of leaves and shrubs, glinting upon swords and spears. And there came upon him, and his disciples, those led by Judas. Then Judas, going forward, kissed the Master's cheek, for he had said to those beside him, "Whoever I kiss, hold him fast." And when they had seized Jesus and bound him, they led him before the High

213

Priests. At the same time, his disciples, being stricken by terror, had fled.

Yet, in a little time, Peter and John, drawn by their own shame, and by love for the Lord, followed after him and awaited him in the common courtyard of the High Priests' palaces. It was told he had declared, before both Annas and Caiaphas, that he was the promised Christ. Whereupon they rent their garments in wrath and horror.

Afterward, they brought him before the Sanhedrin, the great Jewish council, hastily convened, which declared him guilty of blasphemy, and worthy of death. And since none save the Romans might command that a prisoner be executed, they would lead him, at daybreak, before the Roman governor, Pontius Pilate.

For Caiaphas had said to the governor, "It is a matter of treason against Rome." And thus it was the duty of Pilate to hold court.

Truly, they sought his death . . . yet neither John nor Peter believed the governor would condemn him, for though the legions of Rome were harsh and unsparing, the justice of its courts was known to all.

Not until long afterward did John reveal how it was that Jesus, left in the hands of the temple guards and the servants of the High Priests, had been struck and spat upon and mocked. For while these awaited the gathering of the council, they covered the eyes of the prisoner and cried out before him, "Prophesy . . . and tell us who smote you!" and afflicted cruel blows upon him.

Instead, John counseled the women to await him, saying he would return to tell them what had come to pass. Pale and wearied and distressed, he hastened forth into the first glimmer of dawn, nor would he taste of the bread they sought to give him.

XXV.

SHE WENT FORTH WITH THE ARM OF JOHN ABOUT HER SAGGING shoulders, with the weeping voices of Mary Cleophas and Salome and the girl of Magdala in her ears. Yet there was a great numbness upon her, and a sense of unreality, so that she stared before her with unseeing eyes, nor did she perceive what street their way had taken. And any who beheld her, a small and frail woman with the unsteadiness of grief upon her and the black veil of a widow falling down against the pallor of her face, would have said, "Surely this woman goes forth to the funeral rites of one dearer to her heart than life itself. . . ."

There was a sense of utter bewilderment upon her, for she knew not what had come to pass. She knew only that John had returned to them, white and shaken, bidding them come forth with him at once, lest they be too late to behold her son's living face. "For he has been condemned to the cross, and even now, they lead him forth to the place of death beyond the gates. . . ."

Long afterward, she knew how it was that the High Priest Caiaphas had gone before Pilate with sly and contriving words. They had no wish to trouble him, to rouse him from slumber . . . yet his devotion to Roman justice was known, and seeing that the man of Nazareth had spoken treason . . . in truth, the matter would require but a little time. They would not

215

ask of him that a full trial be held, seeing that already, they had found the prisoner guilty and worthy of death. For it was known to them that the governor was allowed to depart from the full Roman legalities when trying a Jew, and might sit as both judge and jury before him, required only to hear the witnesses and pronounce the sentence.

Yet Pontius Pilate, being bitterly aware of their scheming would not have it so. Instead he went forth to the judgment hall, bearing himself sternly, making it plain before them that the accused man would be given a trial in the manner of the searching Roman law. And according to the legal manner of beginning a trial, he asked, "What accusation do you bring against this man?"

Seeing that the feasts of the Passover had strengthened their numbers and their arrogance, those before him answered with insolent cries. He had aroused the people to dissension, they shouted, knowing this to be forbidden by the emperor. He had spoken against the rendering up of tribute, he had declared himself a king.

Yet they would not enter the judgment hall, lest they be made unclean by coming beneath the roof of a Gentile, and forbidden to eat of the sacred feast. Thus, Pilate went out to them again and again, returning each time to the tall young man who awaited him with lifted head and bound hands and the marks of blows upon his face. And Pilate demanded, "Are you a king?" Whereupon the man of Nazareth answered, in quiet tones, "I am a king . . . but my kingdom is not of this world."

In truth, the Roman governor was both perplexed and startled by these words. Yet it was certain in his mind that this quiet young Jew with the clear eyes and the majesty of bearing was no man of evil. Thus, when he had questioned him for a little time, he went forth and said to those who waited, "I find no fault in him."

Whereupon their wrath rose up like the flaring of a flame. "He has stirred up the people." "He has taught words of blasphemy!" "He has spoken treason throughout Judea and Galilee."

And the governor said, "If he is a Galilean, then let him be tried before Herod Antipas . . . ruler of his province!"

For the tetrarch had come up to eat the Passover in Jerusalem and dwelt, with his wife and court, in an ancient palace of kings a little distance beyond. Therefore Jesus was brought before Herod Antipas also, and the tetrarch besought him to do some wonder, that he might look upon his magic. Yet Jesus neither moved nor uttered as much as a word before the man. Whereupon Herod Antipas and those who served him, giving themselves up to jesting and mockery, arrayed the son of Mary in a robe of courtly splendor and returned him to Pontius Pilate.

Then the Roman governor spoke again before the multitude of Jews, despising them in his heart, saying coldly, "I have found no fault with this man, nor has Herod Antipas judged him worthy of death. Therefore, he shall be scourged and released."

Then those who massed before him cried out in voices of hate, "Crucify him!"

The words rendered the governor astonished and aghast. And he demanded in wonder, "Wherefore? What evil has he done?"

Yet, wild and unreasoning, striving forward in disorder, with the rending of their garments, the waving of staves and fists, they called out in a thousand voices, "Let him be crucified!"

For it was plain that there was none among them who believed him to be anointed of God, the Messiah, the Christ to come. Nay, the true Messiah would call down the wrath of the heavens upon any who sought to stay him, would lay waste

217

to his enemies and their own. "Nay, he has deceived us and beguiled us, has put us to shame. . . ."

And they lifted up their cries again and again, in a voice like the roaring of a devouring beast, "Let him be crucified!"

In the season of unleavened bread, it was the custom of the governor to bring forth a prisoner from Antonia Fortress, and release him. A certain Barabbas had been chosen, yet surely, seeing that Barabbas was a man of great evil, the multitude would sooner see him crucified than the man of Nazareth. Therefore the governor cried out to them, "Whom would you have set free . . . this man or Barabbas?" And they shouted wildly, "Barabbas . . . Barabbas!"

It was at this moment that a servant of the palace brought Pontius Pilate word from his wife, a certain Claudia known to all as a woman of great beauty and goodness. By reason of a terrifying dream, an omen of great evil to those of Rome, she had written, "Have nothing to do with this just man. . . ." Stirred by his own fears when he had looked upon the message, the governor cried out, "What then am I to do with him who stands before me?"

And they shouted in a single savage howl: "Crucify him!"

Then Pontius Pilate, pale with hatred of their unreasoning fanaticism, their incessant contentions, asked that a basin of water be brought forth. And he washed his hands before them, according to their own custom. For the washing of the hands was a symbol among the Jewish elders when they declared themselves innocent of bloodguiltiness.

In truth, the rousing of the Jews to dissension was an offense against Rome and, for this, he would sentence the Christ to scourging. It might be that, when this had been accomplished, they would be content, would pity his sufferings, for any man given the punishment of scourging was brought near to death, bruised and welted and broken, streaming with blood from wounds.

Thus the governor sent Jesus forth to be scourged, stripped and bound to a column in the courtyard of the fortress. There came toward him the towering and heavy-muscled torturers, bearing a flagellum—a lash with bits of bone and metal fastened upon its thongs, so that the flesh of the prisoner might be rent and bruised and burst. And they set upon him without mercy, wondering that he did not fall to his death before them, since he had neither eaten nor slept, and was worn utterly by the long hours of torment.

Then, certain of the legionaires gathered about him, with derision and mocking words, arrayed him in a cloak of kingly splendor, thrust into his hand a reed for a scepter, pressed upon his brow a crown hastily wrought of thorns, and cried out in vicious railery, "Hail, King of the Jews!"

Afterward Pontius Pilate led him before the multitude. Yet they had no mercy upon the piteous figure, but howled anew, "Crucify him!" And the governor was stirred by uneasiness, for despite the strength of his troops, they were outnumbered by the howling horde beyond. Yet, out of his devotion to Roman justice, he stood resolute and unyielding, calling forth that Jesus would be released.

Then, suddenly, out of the ominous silence which had fallen upon them, the voice of an elder shouted, "You are not Caesar's friend!"

The man of Nazareth had declared himself a king . . . and none could deny that this was treason. Should he go forth alive, the priests and elders would accuse the governor before Tiberius Caesar, sending a delegation to Rome, pleading the concern of loyal subjects. The governor, being without defense, might himself be recalled, even sent to his death. And, knowing this, he stood stricken and afraid.

"You are not Caesar's friend!"

Thus he gave Jesus up to be crucified.

And now Mary, with John and the Galilean women, came

upon the street and perceived the procession of death approaching. It was led by a Roman soldier riding a great black horse whose hoofs clashed and rang upon the stones of the street. In the midst of guards, Roman legionaries bearing spears, was Jesus . . . followed by two thieves who had been condemned to die this day. He staggered beneath a heavy length of cypress, the beam of his own cross, the carrying of which was required of all condemned to such a death.

The name of each prisoner had been lettered upon a placard to be nailed upon his cross, and was borne before him by a soldier. Long afterward, Mary learned how it was that Pontius Pilate had commanded the words of the placard: *Jesus of Nazareth, King of the Jews.* Yet the elders cried out against him, saying, "Do not write that he is king of the Jews . . . write that he *said* he was king of the Jews!" But Pilate, gazing upon them coldly, said, "What I have written, I have written." Nor would he allow the words to be altered.

Yet, in this moment, Mary beheld none save her son, and looking upon him, cried out in shock and anguish of heart.

His staggering steps had slowed, his face was convulsed by pain and striving, his breath heavy and labored, his flesh and clothing stained with blood from the wounds of the flagellum, rivulets of blood seeping from the thorns upon his brow. A wave of sickness, warm and stupefying, came upon Mary, and she would have fallen, had not the strength of John restored her. Then, stretching forth her hands, she cried out in tones of anguish not to be borne, "My son . . . my son . . . my son. . . ."

The glazing eyes of Jesus perceived that she was beside him. Even in his agony, he sought to speak some word of comfort before her, and yet could not. Seeing her hasten toward him, the guard thrust her back. Yet she stumbled along the narrow walled street, her garments caught and torn by the stones. Behind her, Mary Cleophas and Salome were weeping with wild, uncontrolled sobs. But Mary Magdalene walked, straight and unyielding, her lifted head high, her bearing imperious before the Romans, her eyes filled with hate.

The two thieves moved lightly and without effort. They had slept and eaten bread; neither had been scourged nor given to the hands of torturers. Yet with Jesus, it was not so. He was worn unto death by the long and merciless night, the threats and blows and mockery, the horror of the flagellum, the desertion of those dear to his heart. Already he was faltering in his steps, his breath coming forth in great anguished gasps.

Suddenly, he fell to the earth, the cross beam toppling beside him, crashing upon the stones. For a moment, he lay lifeless before them, and the heart of Mary cried out: Let it be that he is dead . . . let it be that he is dead, and they can torture him no more. . . .

Whereupon one of the soldiers cried out in a voice of anger, "He mocks us! He is not dead, but living! Lift him up and lash him forward!"

And another shouted, with contemptuous laughter, "Behold him who would lead a nation! He has not the strength to lead the way to his own death!"

Petronius, the centurion, had been charged with many a crucifixion. Indeed, crucifixion was a common matter to the legions of the emperor. Once three thousand crosses had been lifted at one time, bringing death to as many Jews. They had risen against their conquerors, and for weeks the air was befouled by the stench of their decayed bodies. In truth, the ways of crucifixion were well known to Petronius and, gazing down, he perceived that the man of Nazareth could bear his cross no farther. Then his eyes well upon a mighty peasant, one Simon of Cyrene. According to the law, any Roman might command a passing Jew to bear a burden for him, and thus Petronius directed the Cyrenian to come forth and take up the beam.

Again the slow and striving procession of death went forward in the sweet April radiance. It was a beautiful day, a festive day, for with the setting of the sun, the feast of the Passover would begin. Among men who waited to be lifted up before their God in holiness of heart, to drink the paschal wine of thanksgiving, these three would be lifted upon the cross of agony, and drink the bitter wine of death.

The city was fragrant with the smoky smell of cooking fires where women toiled at the baking of unleavened bread, at the setting forth of wine and bitter herbs, the preparing of all that was needful for this day, and the Sabbath to come after. Everywhere were the light voices and pleasing tumult and haste of a great festival, save in the street of death where many came forth to look upon the condemned.

Suddenly, there was a cry of anguish and a woman cast herself forward, heedless of the soldiers. It was Veronica, she whom Jesus had healed of an issue of blood, and who had come up to the holy city for the festival. Now, weeping bitterly, she seized the gossamer veil from her head and cleansed his face, seeing that it was stained with blood and sweat and the spittle of many. Whereupon one of the soldiers cursed her and thrust her back, but she followed after, and would not be turned away.

Mary moved through a searing haze of suffering, lifted by the arm of the weeping John. And when they had come to the place of death, he would not have her go forth to the uprights standing ready for the execution, but stayed her, and the women with her, that they should not behold the horror to come. Thus they did not see the prisoners stripped of their garments, save for loincloths, nor did they see the legionaries stretching their arms upon the beams, driving the nails through their wrists. Yet the dull sound of mallets and the screams of the elder thief turned them sick and brought faintness upon them.

Then the crosses were raised and stood against the sky, with the living forms upon them. At the same time a group of Jewish women drew near, garbed in black, bringing a jar and some cups. Being gentlehearted women, righteous and kindly, they could not bear the thought that condemned men should suffer. Thus they made and gave to them a stupefying wine, mingling within it incense and myrrh. Yet when the cup was held forth to Jesus, he would not receive it, for it was written that he must take unto himself the full measure of suffering.

There were many who gathered near, some in hate, some in curiosity, some in sorrow. There were some who believed in him, yet dared utter no words of their faith lest they be set upon and stoned. There were certain men who cried out, "Let us see you save yourself . . . and we shall fall in the dust before you!"

Others shouted, with derision, "If you are the son of God, come down from the cross!"

There were women who turned to their neighbors, saying, "He saved others, yet he cannot save himself." And one declared that he had neither saved nor healed. Nay, it was but a tale spread by the credulous. . . .

And so it was for a length of three incredible hours.

The crosses, with uprights set deeply in the earth, were so low that those of the multitude spat upon the faces of the dying. It was said that the crucified bodies must be taken from them before night, lest they be assailed by jackals and pariah dogs out of the wilderness. Thus, when Mary and the others came forward, they could gaze into the eyes of the beloved, and their own pain became light and bearable before the measure of his suffering. Yet, even at the edge of death, he did not cease to know concern for her who had borne him and, speaking to John, said, "Behold your mother." And to Mary he whispered, through swollen and bleeding lips, "Woman . . . behold your son."

Then one of the thieves, a certain Gestas, a gross and brutal scoundrel, began to rail against him, mocking him.

"If you are the Messiah, save yourself and us!"

But Dismas, the other, a comely man with the blood of the desert in his veins, reproached him, saying, "We are justly condemned . . . but this man is without sin." Slowly, against his own suffering, he turned his head so that his gaze might rest upon the face of the holy one beside him. And in a voice broken by penitence, he pled, "Lord, when you come into your kingdom, remember me."

Then Jesus, even as he suffered the anguish, the thirst, the pain, had compassion upon him and answered, "Verily I say unto you, today you shall be with me in paradise."

Dismas was now beyond the strength to speak further, but a look of deliverance came into his eyes, a radiance glorified his face. Even as Mary gazed upon him, startled into remembrance, his head fell forward upon his chest, and the light of the sun disclosed to her the scar upon his face, long and thin, wrought by a claw of the wilderness, unmistakable, unforgotten, the mark of the Little Robber.

XXVI.

THE WOMAN HAD STUMBLED FORTH INTO THE NIGHT, UNABLE TO abide longer within the darkened house, where the phantoms of her dead son rose before her eyes, tenuous and dissolving, like the mists which floated in from the valleys and obscured the plains, after the going down of the sun.

For a time, she had lain upon her bed mat, shattered and unmoving, thinking to divide herself from' her own anguish of heart by the merciful oblivion of slumber. Yet she was unable to prevail against the image of the beloved one hanging in ghastly and infamous death against the soft spring sky. Thus, driven to her feet by the violence of her sorrow, she rose and paced the length of the room, again and yet again, times without number, her pale lips murmuring words dull and insensate, scarcely more than the syllables of a moan, "Nay, nay . . . it cannot be . . . not of him . . . my son, my son. . . ."

The house was no longer to be endured, its stifling darkness, the known emptiness, the heavy and oppressive stillness. Thus she paused before the clothes chest and reached within it, seeking certain familiar folds with numb and groping fingers, drawing forth a dark cloak which she cast about her shoulders, shrouding her hair. A woman did not go forth alone after the fall of darkness, but she would go forth. A worthy mother did not flee from her own anguish of heart,

225

stumbling down the silent Jerusalem streets, through sheltered darkness and streaming moonlight and the sharp, clean shadows of leaves and boughs. Yet she was fleeing.

The sound of her sandals, brushing the stirred dust and worn stones, was loud in the utter desolation of the empty street, as though the hour were very late. Yet it was not long past the rising of the moon. Lamps yet gleamed from many windows, and the sound of voices rose in quiet talk and murmurous laughter behind certain casements and lattices. And over the holy city, spreading even into the distant hills, was a fragrance sweet and nostalgic, the smell of wood smoke risen from a thousand supper fires.

Yet so dulled by weeping were her senses, so disordered by agony her thoughts, that it was necessary for her to halt her aimless steps, to stand quietly in the moonlit street, as dark and tragic a figure as death itself, pressing one hand against her brow, as she sought to recall the reason for so great an abundance of smoke. And suddenly it came upon her with the lashing strength of a blow. It was the night of the Passover and many had remained within the city, that they might talk of the death of him who was called Jesus of Nazareth, before they turned homeward from their pilgrimage. And she said to herself: Many who sit with their brethren in this hour, feasting and merry, were of the throng which cried out for the death of Jesus, this same morning, before the judgment seat of Rome. And she departed from them with deep and choking sobs, striving forward in the manner of one wounded and pursued.

And now the phantoms of remembrance returned to her again and would not be put aside. She looked upon the face of her son when he had been laid in her arms, swaddled in lengths of linen from his chest to his feet. She recalled the small and beautiful face, roseate and warm, the great dark eyes, the thick black ringlets of hair. And, gazing upon him, she had said in her heart: Truly this child is chosen of the Lord. And there had flowed forth from her heart, with the radiance of song, the lovely words of the psalmist: *"Oh, give thanks unto the Lord, for He is good, and His mercy endures forever. . . ."*

She recalled how it was that they had borne the child forth from the village, that he might be presented in the temple of Jerusalem, how she had been certain in her heart that all who beheld them looked with wondering eyes and yearning arms upon her babe.

And now one image, and then another, rose before her wide and unseeing eyes, called forth from the chambers of her treasured years. She beheld the fair white tunic which she had woven for his presentation at the synagogue, how she had led him forth to the master with both pride and sorrow, knowing that the years of his schooling would draw him farther from her side.

She thought of certain games which had enlivened the years of his boyhood, the reed pipes and whistles he had fashioned, the slingshots which had found such favor in his eyes that he had become uncommonly skilled in their handling . . . indeed, could sever a twig from a branch.

And the Feast of the Ingathering . . . again she knew how it was that he had taken delight in the small tabernacle contrived from leafy boughs, raised in the swept courtyard beneath the shadow of the fig tree. She could behold him passing in and out, after the manner of a pleased child, calling his companions to witness the excellence of the shelter, the wonder of his mother's skill.

It was known throughout the village that he was a lad uncommonly quick at learning, and her kinsmen had gazed upon him with pride no less than her own, seeing him declare before them, "Hear, O Israel, the Lord our God is one God. . . ."

And now the thought of certain Passover nights returned to her . . . the yellow radiance of the supper fires, the savory

227

smell of the lamb, the sight of her son, small and comely, lifting his great dark eyes to the assembled company, chosen to ask, in his childish voice, the ritual query: "Wherefore is this night different from all other nights?"

There were many among the women of the village who declared, "This child shall bear witness to the Lord!" Yet she had uttered no portion of what was in her heart, lest they consider her pride in him vain and unseemly.

Long afterward, when he had come to the years of his manhood and had gone forth with the Twelve, that he might glorify God, she had known such joy of fulfillment as came to few mothers in Israel. Yet now there was, within her heart, only the anguish of an ancient cry: *"O God, hear the words of my prayer! Hide me under the shadow of Thy wings. . . ."*

Pale and unhurried clouds had risen in the sky and now, suddenly, the moon burst through them, falling upon her face with a radiance which summoned her back to reality. She perceived that she had come a long distance, had returned even to her own house, where the door stood open upon the empty room, the cold hearth, the dreamless slumber. . . .

And she spoke aloud, saying what was not to be believed. "He is dead. I shall never look upon his face again. . . ." And she said to herself that she wished he might have died, simply, sweetly, in the years of his childhood.

Suddenly, tears filled her eyes and ran, swift and scalding, down her pale cold face. Wherefore had he died so shameful a death . . . wherefore had he sought so terrible a destiny? Oh, my son . . . *my son* . . . numbered with the evil, despised in the eyes of the multitude. . . . Lord, show mercy upon him, and upon my broken heart. . . .

And she cast herself down upon the path before her door and mingled her tears with the dust and struck her hands upon the earth. Then, drawn by the sound of her terrible weeping, two women hastened forth from the house beside her own and beheld the dark and shattered figure lying in the moonlight upon the stones. And the first would have knelt at her side, but the other would not have it so.

"Nay," she said quietly, "do not go forth. For it is the mother of Judas who lies at our feet, and there is naught we can do to stay her tears."

XXVII.

Obscurely, as though from a great distance, it came to Mary that Salome was striving to draw her away from the scene. Yes, truly, it was the voice of her faithful sister, broken by sorrow, rendered hoarse from weeping, seeking to persuade her.

"It is finished. He is dead. Let me lead you forth from this place of horror. . . ."

She has grown old, Mary thought dully. Behold, her eyes are sunken in shadow, her face seamed and thick and pale, like leavened dough. And her mouth has ceased to possess a shape, but gapes like an open wound. . . .

And now Mary Cleophas came forward shaken by such anguish of heart that her words trembled upon her lips. And Mary said to herself: We have all grown old. Our hands, clinging together, are dry as the dust of the tomb. . . .

"My sister," Mary Cleophas was pleading, "let us go forth a little distance. I would not have you look upon him when they . . . they lift him from the cross. . . ."

Mary stared at her, unanswering. He is dead. His agonies are ended. Wherefore should I suffer now?

Then she felt an arm about her shoulders, an arm young and firm-fleshed and tender. And, with the gentleness of youth for the sorrows and infirmities of years, Mary Magdalene led her away. There were no tears upon the face of the girl, nor had she wept. Her eyes were like stones, her face set in lines of bitterness chilling to behold. Yet, turning to Mary, she spoke gently and with tenderness.

They led her to some rocks near a garden and there she waited, in the midst of them, until John should return from the cross.

And now she perceived that two elders, men of dignity and bearing, with faces of righteousness and wisdom, had gone forth to the cross. Mary Magdalene murmured that they were Nicodemus and Joseph of Arimathea, one a Pharisee, the other a Sadducee, who many times heard the teachings of Jesus, and had spoken with him. Both were of the Sanhedrin, yet they had become followers of Jesus in secret, and both had sought to spare him from death.

Now they came forth boldly, giving no heed, in their grief, to those who might behold them and hasten before the priests with word of their blasphemy. For earlier, Joseph of Arimathea had gone to the palace, wherein the Roman governor dwelt when he visited Jerusalem, and asked that he might be received. And, being brought before Pilate, Joseph said, "My Lord, let us look with pity upon the dead. For, seeing that he has no tomb, I would place the body of Jesus of Nazareth in that prepared for me, in my own garden, a new tomb wherein none has been laid. . . ."

And Pilate gave him leave, that this might be done.

Now he and Nicodemus walked swiftly to the crosses, followed by servants who bore fine linens for shrouding the beloved one, a jar of water from the well, a hundredweight in burial spices, the pungent aloes and myrrh.

Gorged with hate and vengeance, wearied by the long vigil of death, those who watched had moved away, singly and in groups, so that now only a few remained. John, Nicodemus and Joseph lifted the body from the cross, placing it gently upon the length of a flat stone nearby.

And now Mary rose to her feet and came forth to her son, nor could any turn her aside. Kneeling beside him, she lifted him in her arms and laid her face against his head and wept heart-shattering tears. And her heart cried out within her: Oh, my son, my son . . . where are your disciples? Where are those who followed after you, declaring they would die for your sake? Where are the blind who see, the lame who walk, the sick who were healed by your compassion? Wherefore have they fled from you in this bitter hour?

In truth, it was as John had said, "He came unto his own, and his own received him not. . . ."

Leaning down to her, Joseph of Arimathea spoke gently, saying that they must hasten with the burial, for the feast of the Passover would begin with the going down of the sun, and to deal with the dead after this hour was to be rendered unclean. Thus she drew apart, that they might do all which needed to be done.

Gently, Joseph and John washed the face of Jesus and smoothed the disordered hair. They bound his head with linen, that the mouth might be closed, and washed the blood and dried sweat and grime from the bruised and torn body. When this had been done, they anointed him with the burial spices and wrapped him in a winding sheet, and bound him with strips of linen, according to the custom.

The garden of Joseph of Arimathea was a place of quiet beauty where a sepulcher had been wrought from a hill of stone. Stooping before the low opening, one might enter a double chamber, the first a small room having a low bench where mourners might sit near their loved dead. Beyond was a large square chamber which contained a rock ledge for the repose of the departed one.

Here the body of the Lord was tenderly borne, placed upon the ledge which, being higher at one end, lifted the head a little. Then John summoned the women, that they might behold him. They entered slowly, Mary going to him first, the others following, and when they had kissed his brow, they laid the linen square upon his face and went from him, weeping desolately.

Then Joseph and Nicodemus and John, with all the strength between them, rolled the great closing stone before the mouth of the tomb. Afterward, the two older men, the Pharisee and the Sadducee, brought together by love of the Lord, bade the women a seemly farewell and, turning from their broken words of gratitude, went forth to the city in the fading light.

A thousand supper fires gleamed upon the hills around Jerusalem where pilgrims without number ate the feast of the Passover in joyous gatherings. And in the light of festive lamps gleaming from the holy city, ancient words echoed from the ancient walls. "This is the poor bread which our fathers ate in the land of Egypt. Let anyone who is hungry come and eat. Let anyone who is needy come and make the Passover. . . ."

They had thought to find the house of Joanna cold and without light, yet lamps had been kindled on the table, coals cast warmth from a braizer, and Mara, a certain neighbor, had borne to them both meat and new bread, seeking to comfort them somewhat. And when she and Joanna had wept together, she told them what had come to pass concerning Judas, the disciple whose greed betrayed the son of Mary.

He had not forseen that this evil would bring death upon the Master, doubtless believing that the authorities would no more than scourge the Galilean teacher, or cast him forth from the city. And when he perceived the enormity of his deed, he had been stricken with terror and repentance.

Therefore, he returned to the priests the thirty pieces of silver, and wept, "I have sinned. . . . I have betrayed innocent blood. . . ."

But they gazed upon him coldly and without compassion.

"What is that to us?" they asked. "It concerns you alone."

Whereupon he cast the pieces of silver down before them and, in an anguish of repentance, rushed forth from the temple and hanged himself.

When Mara had departed to her own house, the women sought, for the sake of kindness, to eat of the food she had borne to them. Yet they could not and thus, after a little time, lay down upon their bed mats, quenching the lamps, striving for peace.

Being wearied beyond the telling, Mary Cleophas and Salome fell into troubled slumber. Yet Mary could not prevail against the images which rose before her closed eyes . . . the convulsed and bleeding countenance of her son, the legionaries dividing his garments at the foot of the cross, casting lots for the seamless robe her hands had wrought for him. She recalled how it was that, even in the extremity of his mortal anguish, he had remembered her loneliness, and given her to the care of John, speaking to the beloved disciple through blue and stiffened lips, "Behold your mother. . . ." Afterward, when all was ended, a certain soldier, desiring to be sure of his death, had plunged a spear into his side. *And thine own soul a sword shall pierce. . . .* For she had witnessed all that came to pass.

A strange darkness had fallen upon the city in that hour, and many stared into the sky and murmured uneasily among themselves. Some declared it a sandstorm out of the desert, quenching the light of the sun, for such storms were not uncommon in the season of spring. Yet others cried out that a sandstorm of such darkness had never been known, and turned homeward in haste and fear. Then there came upon the city a sudden violence, so that the earth was shaken, and a sound of thunder rose from the bowels of the earth. Whereupon, the centurion, starting up, cried out before the dead Jesus,

"Truly this man was a son of God!" And wept in shame and horror before his own deed.

Now, brilliant white moonlight was slanting into the room, and in its radiance, Mary perceived the form of the unsleeping girl of Magdala. Throughout the day she had not wept, and now her eyes had the fixed and wounded stare of one who looks upon an evil dream. And presently, out of the darkness and silence, the mother of Jesus turned to the most faithful of his followers.

"Mary . . ."

The girl stirred, yet no word passed her lips.

"Mary, except you weep, your sorrow will destroy you utterly."

Still, the girl said nothing, though her lips quivered.

"He is dead, and they can torture him no more. Let us give thanks for this mercy and know that, even now, his love has not departed from us. . . ."

The girl uttered a small, whimpering cry and crept like an animal to Mary's side, resting against her. Mary held her close, smoothing her soft bright hair. And suddenly the girl of Magdala burst into such an agony of weeping that, when at length it had passed, she lay limp and unmoving. A little time later, she slept.

Mary drew a coverlet upon the girl and sat gazing down at her.

For her, I have found peace, she thought, but not for myself. God of mercy, how may I cease to think of him in the cold and silent loneliness of dust and myrrh?

XXVIII.

ALL NIGHT THEY HAD WAITED FOR THE DAWN, TORMENTED BY the changing, restive slumber of those whose flesh is aware of their sorrowing spirit.

Now the first tremulous stirring of day was heard in the palm fronds moved by the wind of the Lord. Slowly, the darkness lifted, became a pale green radiance glimmering along the casements and in the narrow streets. Within the upper chamber of Joanna's house, shapes emerged from the dimness, edged with uncertain light, a cedarwood chest, a great earthenware bowl, a low table, a copper brazier.

Abruptly the dawn rays were lifted up on the wings of morning, above the pearly mists of the valleys, the unsown blossoms opening in the tender grasses. Beyond the city, amid the barren slopes, the strengthening radiance brought into being the solemn green of the wild olives, the silent stones, the smoky thorn.

Then all the splendor of dawn was cast, like a roseate veil, upon the ancient streets, and numberless birds lifted up their voices in the timeless cadences of spring.

Mary opened her eyes and, gazing slowly about the unfamiliar room, was stricken with swift and unsparing desolation. He is dead. Even now, he lies within the rock-hewn chamber. . . . And her heart was leaden within her, as though it, too, had become a burden of clay.

236

He is dead. God of mercy, how was it that the stars had not fallen from the sky, the sun turned into darkness, all rejoicing and radiance and laughter perished before the magnitude of that which had come to pass? It was not to be believed that the earth was unchanged, the pattern of its days unaltered and serene. Yet, from the walls of the Roman fortress there rose the sound of the trumpets which made known the changing of the guard. In the golden temple, the faithful awaited the rising of the sun, that they might begin the chanting of an ancient orison: "Blessed be the eternal God who has created light and darkness. . . ."

From the courtyard beneath came the voices of doves, muted and compelling, even as in the days of her childhood. The thin and unhurried clouds of spring rose up behind the palms beyond the casement. On the plains beyond, there came forth, out of the parting mists and paling shadows, the caravans of the ungodly, moving through the stilled peace of the radiant morning toward the great market of Damascus. On the slopes of the wilderness, shepherds led their flocks forth to the blessed abundance of spring. It was as though he who lay within the sealed darkness of the tomb had never trodden the earth. And such anguish assailed her at the thought that she wept in inconsolable grief.

For two nights, the women of Galilee had shared the great upper chamber, that they might comfort one another by their nearness. Yet now, Mary was utterly alone. The others had stolen forth in the first light of day, forbearing to rouse her from her troubled slumber, quenching the flame of the lamp, stirring the ashes of the brazier, so that warmth emerged from it, and a pale radiance. But the light fragrance of wood smoke was lost entirely in the odor of burial spices and unguents which lay upon the house with the dread heaviness of a pall.

On the afternoon of the day just past, Mary Magdalene and

Salome had gone down to the great Jerusalem market, seeking more spices. For that Jesus should have been borne to the tomb with such a measure of haste and disorder was a wound upon them all. Thus, out of her own substance, Mary Magdalene had purchased the most costly of fragrant herbs and nards.

Last night, the evening bread had remained untasted upon the board. And when they had lain themselves down in the dim light of the lamp, after the going down of the sun, they had spoken together in low and broken tones of the beloved. Yet no word concerning the apostles fell from their lips, seeing that all save the faithful John had fled into hiding. The face of Mary Cleophas was swollen with shamed weeping, that the sons in which she had come to know such pride had deserted the Lord in the hour of his affliction. For even those slow of thought and word were dear to his heart.

James, the son of Zebedee, had been bold and striving all the days of his life, even as his companions, the fiery Peter, the resolute Andrew, the guileless Philip and Nathanael, the simplehearted Thomas, faithful Matthew, and the zealous one known as Simon, the Canaanite. Among them were men said to be sons of fire and thunder, of spirit and ardor. Yet John alone, who was gentle and without daring, had stood unflinching before the clamoring throng, strengthened by love for him who was nailed upon the cross. In John, Salome could take comfort, even while she sorrowed for his fainthearted brother.

In truth, it was not unnatural that the apostles should fear the wrath of the authorities. Yet, seeing that the tumult had been thrust aside to make way for the Feast of Unleavened Bread, there was no talk of seizing those who had been followers of Jesus of Nazareth. Thus John had gone forth to seek them, believing they had concealed themselves in known hiding places on the Mount of Olives. He would strive to persuade them, he said, to return to the upper room in which they had eaten the last supper with the Lord, and which was still open to them. Whereupon Salome answered bitterly that they would doubtless come forth without reluctance, for the sake of their own hunger.

Even after she had risen and garbed herself, Mary could not go forth with the bitterness upon her, but stood at the casement, staring out over the roofs of the city. And she said to herself: Even the pagans who dwell within this land have believed in the coming of the Messiah. Out of the mouths of the prophets had come words which those of Israel had cherished and taught throughout countless generations. And even as she had uttered them in the days of her childhood, so now she brought them forth from the chambers of her memory.

"And thou, Bethlehem . . . out of thee shall come forth one who is to be ruler in Israel.

"Then the eyes of the blind shall see, and the ears of the deaf shall be unstopped. Then shall the lame man leap as a hart, and the tongues of the dumb shall sing.

"Behold, thy king cometh unto thee. He is just and having salvation, lowly, and riding upon a colt, the foal of an ass. . . .

"He is brought as a sheep to the slaughter, and as a sheep before the shearers, he is dumb . . . he was taken from the prison and the judgment . . . and he made his grave with the wicked and the rich . . . though he had done no violence . . . neither was any deceit in him. . . .

"He was numbered with the transgressors, and made intercession for them.

"Reproach has broken my heart . . . they gave me gall for my meat, and in my thirst they gave me vinegar to drink.

"My God, my God, why have you forsaken me? They have parted my garments among them, and upon my vesture they cast lots. . . ."

All these and more were written in the holy scriptures. And she said to herself that all men seek after a sign, yet even

239

should this be held forth to them, they would not receive it. Then, out of her anguish and despair rose the unvoiced cry, "Wherefore did the Lord abandon His son to agony and death?"

Abruptly, the thought of Joseph came to her, and the memory of the words he had spoken before her, on a certain fair morning more than thirty summers past. "Then I said to myself: Who am I to say what is to be or not to be? For I am but a man, and it is not for me to judge the holy will of God . . . but only to perform it."

And the lovely face of Elizabeth rose before her eyes, the gracious voice of Elizabeth spoke on the murmur of the stirring wind. "Wait upon the Lord . . . be of good courage . . . and he shall strengthen your heart."

Thus were the living counseled by the dead, out of the unforgotten past, the unforsaken memories, the stream of eternal wisdom flowing from generation to generation.

Suddenly, from below, she heard the sounds of arrival, the mingled voices of her sisters, and it was borne in upon her that going to the tomb had strengthened their sorrow. For they were weeping in harsh and unrestrained sobs, assailed by an agony of spirit shattering to look upon. She hastened to go forth to them, then, gazing with pity upon the shoulders bowed beneath the burdens of years, the toilworn hands, the greying hair. Yet when she strove to comfort them, Salome lifted a tear-ravaged face and cried out in tones abandoned and terrible, "They have taken away the Lord . . . and we know not where they have laid him!"

Mary drew apart from them, staring, stricken into silence, a dazed weakness upon her.

"Nay . . ." she said, and could speak no word further.

They wept anew, saying how it was that even as they went forth, considering whether the gardener might be prevailed upon to uncover the tomb, they perceived that the stone had been rolled away, and the mouth of the chamber revealed. In shock and fright, they had cast the spices from them and hastened to look within, beholding the linen graveclothes, and the white square which had covered the face of Jesus. Then, stricken to the heart that such a thing had come about, Salome and Mary Cleophas turned homeward, crying aloud as they went, but Mary Magdalene was too anguished by grief to depart, and they had left her weeping against the stone.

Yet scarcely had the words come forth from their lips when the girl Mary Magdalene appeared in the doorway, nor was there any sorrow upon her, but only a great wonder and a radiance of utter joy. Then, breathless because she had run to them, and because of the exaltation upon her, she cried, *"I have seen the Lord!"*

And she told how it had come to pass that while she wept beside the tomb, a voice had spoken to her saying, "Woman, wherefore do you weep? Whom are you seeking?"

In truth, she had believed the man to be the gardener. And, unable to lift her head because of her grief, she answered in the syllables of the brokenhearted, "Sir, if you have borne him hence, tell me where you have laid him, and I will take him away. . . ."

There was a little space of silence. Then the voice spoke again, with tenderness and compassion.

"Mary. . . ."

It was a voice known to her ears, beloved in her heart, and hearing it, she cried aloud, *"Master!"* And when she had flung herself down before him, that she might embrace his feet, he said to her, "Touch me not, for I have not yet ascended to my Father . . . but go forth and say to my brethren that I ascend to my Father and their Father, to my God and their God." And he departed from her.

Whereupon she had run fleetly and joyously down the garden path still dampened by the dews of night, past the drip-

241

ping boughs and flowering shrubs, through shafts of radiance and depths of shadow, away from the tomb, forth to the empty streets, and to the house of Joanna.

Her words brought such joy upon the other women that they no longer wept, but lifted up their heads and hearts and gazed at one another with shining eyes, and said, "The end is not come . . . he is not dead, but risen. . . ." And strove to believe that they spoke out of faith restored, and not out of the anguish of their yearning.

Near the going down of the sun, John returned from the Mount of Olives, and with him all those who had fled, men wordless and sorrowing, their eyes reddened by tears. Indeed, they appeared only a little less wretched than the beggars at the gate, their garments sullied by the rents and dust of flight, their faces marked by weariness and hunger and stunned despair. Yet even as they entered, their shame was lifted up and cast from them by the voices of the rejoicing women, crying out the tidings of the Lord.

Then Peter and John, openly doubting that the girl of Magdala had spoken truth, sped forth to the tomb but John, by reason of his youth and lightness, came to it first. And, returning, they acknowledged that it was as they had been told, empty save for the graveclothes, and the linen square laid apart. Yet they murmured among themselves, unwilling to receive all that Mary Magdalene had spoken. Surely the High Priests and Pharisees had borne the body of Jesus from the garden. Nay, John declared, for when Pilate had given them leave, the High Priests and Pharisees sealed the stone and set a guard to watch over the tomb by night, saying, "lest his disciples come and steal him away, and say to the people, He is risen. . . ." And if indeed he had come forth from death, wherefore had he appeared, not to them, but to a woman, asking that she bear witness to his word? For it was known to all that women were humble and without authority.

242

Yet, being heartened and comforted by the thought of Jesus risen and returned to them, the apostles cast their gloom from them, washed and put on cleanly garments, sat at the spread board. And afterward, all of the company gathered in the upper room, that they might speak further of him whom they loved, and pray together.

Darkness had fallen upon the city. The hour was late. There was but a single lamp within the room, and the doors had been made fast against the night, seeing that the apostles had not ceased to fear the vengeance of the Pharisees. Then Peter, lifting up his voice before the Lord, uttered the words of an ancient prayer of contrition: "O, Lord, rebuke us not in thine anger, neither chastise us, but have mercy upon us, for we are weak. . . ." And afterward, they prayed together: "God be merciful to us and bless us, and cause His face to shine upon us. . . ."

And when they lifted up their eyes, behold, Jesus stood in the midst of them.

Nor was he a spirit of the dead, but one risen in the flesh, garbed as they had beheld him times without number, in the girdled tunic, the sandals, the white kaffiyeh upon his head. And his voice, low and gentle, uttered the familiar words of his lips.

"Peace be unto you."

Mary's heart leapt within her bosom, her breath was quickened in her throat, her spirit cried out in voiceless wonder, "My son, my son. . . ." And as he turned to her, his hands held forth to her, his face radiant with the love he bore her, it was as if he had spoken again the cherished name, the tenderest word in the whole of their language, "*Woman.* . . ."

243